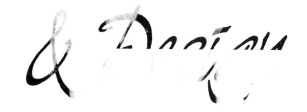

Textiles Fabric & Design

JUDY VULKER AND HELEN COOPER

HEINEMANN BOOKS

Heinemann Educational Books Ltd
22 Bedford Square, London WC1B 3HH

LONDON   EDINBURGH   MELBOURNE
AUCKLAND   SINGAPORE
KUALA LUMPUR   NEW DELHI
IBADAN   NAIROBI   JOHANNESBURG
PORTSMOUTH (NH) KINGSTON

First published in Australia by The Macmillan Company of
Australia Pty Ltd, 1985

This revised edition first published in Great Britain by
Heinemann Educational Books, 1987
Reprinted 1988

British Library Cataloguing in Publication Data

Vulker, Judy
   Textiles, fabric & design.
   1. Textile crafts
   I. Title   II. Cooper, Helen
   746   TT699

ISBN 0 435 42899 3

Printed in Great Britain by Thomson Litho Ltd, East Kilbride,
Scotland

Contents

Preface

Textiles, Fabric & Design was written for secondary school Textile and Design courses in Australia.

It has been revised for use in the UK and will serve as a useful source of information for course work studies for the GCSE and Standard Grade Textiles examinations. It will also be useful as a reference book for lower secondary pupils.

The text is easy to read and well illustrated. Each chapter concludes with revision exercises, extension activities and suggestions for further reading.

Introduction

What is a fibre?

A fibre is the basic raw material used in the production of yarn. Fibres from natural sources are usually short, from 15 to 140 mm.

Silk is an exception, because it has a very long fibre. This type of fibre is called a *filament*.

Fibre extraction from a yarn

Activity

Try to extract fibres from different types of yarns. You will notice that some fibres are longer than others; they may also be thick, thin, shiny, fluffy, strong, weak or wrinkled. (These are all *properties* of fibres.)

How would you describe the fibres you have extracted?

What is a yarn?

A yarn is made by twisting fibres together to form a strand. The twisting is important, as it makes fibres strong enough to be used to weave or knit a fabric.

Yarns may be twisted or *spun* tightly or loosely. Many fibres may be used to make a thick yarn; a few fibres to make a thin yarn.

Fibres are twisted to make a yarn.

Activity

Try to make yarns by twisting some fibres together. What properties do the fibres have now?

What is a fabric?

Fabrics are made by weaving, knitting or bonding yarns together. (These processes are discussed in Chapter 6.)

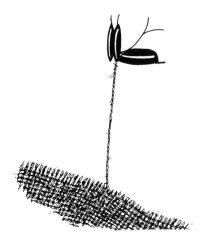

A yarn being pulled from fabric

Activity

Compare the properties of fabrics that are woven, knitted and bonded. Pull the fabric widthways, lengthways and diagonally. Do the fabrics fall apart easily? Look closely at each fabric, and sketch its construction. Which is the weakest type of fabric? Why?

Natural and man-made fibres

Fibres are of two main types: those made from materials that occur in nature and those made by chemical or other means in a laboratory.

Natural fibres

- *Animal,* e.g. wool, silk, hair (camel, mohair, goat, alpaca)
- *Vegetable,* e.g. cotton, flax, hemp, jute, ramie, sisal
- *Mineral,* e.g. asbestos, metallic fibres (gold, aluminium, silver such as Lurex*)

Man-made fibres

- *Regenerated cellulosic fibres,* e.g. acetate, triacetate, cuprammonium rayon, viscose rayon, polnosic rayon, alginate

- *Synthetic fibres*
  — Polyamides, e.g. nylon, Bri-Nylon*
  — Polyesters, e.g. Terylene*, Dacron*, Trevira*, Crimplene*
  — Polyacrylics, e.g. Orlon*, Acrilan*, Courtelle*, Dralon*
  — Polyurethanes, e.g. elastofibres such as Spanzelle*, Lycra*
  — Polyolefines, e.g. polythene such as Courlene*

* Trade names of fibres or fabrics made from these fibres.

Until 100 years ago, only natural fibres were used to make fabrics. Today, with the development of man-made fibres, we have a wide variety of fibres to choose from.

Natural fibres can be blended with man-made fibres to make fabrics. This may produce a cloth with advantages that neither fibre had separately. For example, sporting clothes and school shirts are often made from a polyester and cotton blend fabric. They require little ironing, because the polyester is wrinkle resistant, yet are comfortable to wear on hot days, because, as a natural fibre, cotton is absorbent and 'breathes'.

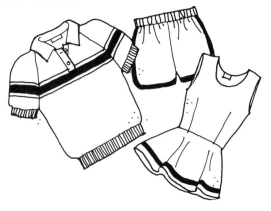

Regenerated and synthetic fibres

Regenerated fibres have an animal (protein) or vegetable (cellulose) base, whereas synthetic fibres are made from chemicals only (usually a derivative of coal or oil).

Activity

Using the classification of fibres on page 2, complete the following crossword.

Across

4 A regenerated cellulosic fibre made from seaweed (8)
6 A polyester (8)
9 The basic raw material used in the manufacture of yarn (5)
10 A vegetable fibre (5)
11 An animal fibre (4)
12 A metallic fibre (5)

Down

1 A vegetable fibre (5)
2 An animal fibre (5)
3 A polyolefine (7)
4 . . . are used as a source of fibres for clothing in South America (7)
5 An animal fibre (4)
7 When fibres are twisted together, they form a . . . (4)
8 A polyamide (5)
9 A vegetable fibre used to make linen (4)
10 An animal fibre (4)

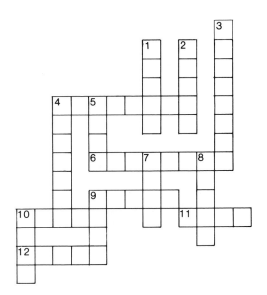

1

Fashion and society

Style

The similarity of dress in many countries today is a consequence of technology, which has improved communication and transport and therefore made people more aware of what is happening in other parts of the world. Many countries still maintain their *traditional dress*, however — a style of clothing that has remained basically unchanged for many generations.

Clothing styles develop for many reasons. The three main reasons are *protection, modesty* and *adornment*.

Protection

Protection is the main reason that people wear clothes. In the first place, they need protection from the climate. For example, many people live in countries where the temperature is extremely hot, such as in desert areas, or extremely cold, such as in the Antarctic regions.

In early times, people developed various forms of armour to protect themselves from human enemies.

Today, in our society, protection is needed in particular by people in dangerous or dirty occupations, such as firemen, astronauts and mechanics.

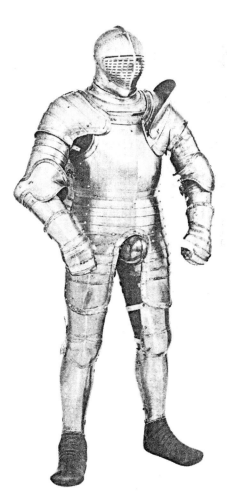

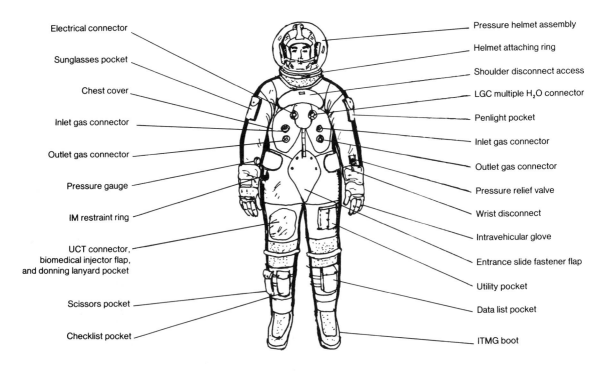

Electrical connector
Sunglasses pocket
Chest cover
Inlet gas connector
Outlet gas connector
Pressure gauge
IM restraint ring
UCT connector, biomedical injector flap, and donning lanyard pocket
Scissors pocket
Checklist pocket

Pressure helmet assembly
Helmet attaching ring
Shoulder disconnect access
LGC multiple H$_2$O connector
Penlight pocket
Inlet gas connector
Outlet gas connector
Pressure relief valve
Wrist disconnect
Intravehicular glove
Entrance slide fastener flap
Utility pocket
Data list pocket
ITMG boot

A space suit is pressurised to allow the wearer to breathe. What other clothing types are similar to this?

Modesty

Modesty means different things in different societies. It depends on the values of that society. Most people in this country would ensure their bodies were reasonably covered when shopping but would consider it acceptable to wear a very brief bikini on the beach. Moslem women in Kuwait cover themselves in a black garment so people cannot see them. In some areas of Africa women are normally naked from the waist up.

Adornment

All societies display a need to decorate the human body. People decorate themselves to indicate status, group identity and for ceremonial display.

Many objects are used for decoration. In more primitive societies, they include teeth or tusks of animals, feathers, bones and clay or ochre.

In some societies, people decorate themselves by painful means, such as tattooing, piercing the skin and cicatrisation (scarring of the skin).

To indicate *group identity*, people wear the same decoration or item of dress, for example a badge or a school uniform.

Activity

(1) Divide the class into three groups.
(2) Each group is to collect pictures to illustrate one of the three main reasons for wearing clothes. Try to find different examples from those illustrated or mentioned here.

times during the week a person may be a student, a tennis player, a first aid officer at a sports ground and a waiter.

Often, the role we are playing is shown by our clothes — our school uniform, tennis gear and so on. In some cases it is particularly important that people performing certain roles — such as police and ambulance officers and hospital staff — can be identified readily.

Traditional Maori costume of New Zealand.

(3) Choose a person from each group to present the illustrations to the class.
(4) With the help of your teacher, make a notice board display using all the illustrations.

Roles

In the normal course of life most people play a number of roles. For example, at different

Activity

(1) List ten jobs that involve people playing a particular role in their daily life.
(2) Beside each, explain briefly what the person in that job has to do to fulfil the role.
(3) Collect illustrations of or draw five costumes that show that a person is performing a particular role.

The changing shapes of fashion

Fashion changes constantly, helping to maintain interest in this area of the market place. Changes in fashion are influenced by many things, including:

- People in the public eye, such as royalty, pop and film stars
- The First World War
- The Industrial Revolution
- Fashion houses and designers.

People in the public eye

Until the early part of this century, the royal families set fashion trends, because they were influential and had plenty of money to spend on clothes.

Queen Elizabeth II has a chief dressmaker, Norman Hartnell, whose dresses feature imaginative touches and exquisite embroidery. Original in decoration more than style, Queen Elizabeth has never been a trendsetter. Princess Diana, on the other hand, has set a number of trends, including frilly blouses and low-heeled shoes.

The Princess of Wales has had great impact as a fashion leader.

The rock band 'Kiss' use clothing and make-up to produce an identity.

Nowadays, fashion leadership has more and more passed to film stars and pop stars and, to a lesser extent, people in politics. Some examples are:

- The pop band Kiss started a fad of bizarre clothes and face painting.
- The tight lycra pants worn by Olivia Newton-John in the movie *Grease* became popular with teenagers.
- Pop groups have popularised smart casual wear.

The First World War

The First World War marked a turning point in fashion, especially female fashion. Many women were required to work outside the home for the first time, to do the jobs formerly done by the men then at war. They worked in factories, delivered mail and worked on farms and properties, among other jobs.

Clothing therefore needed to be more functional. Hems began to rise to calf length, and clothes began to follow the form of the female

Olivia Newton-John and John Travolta in the movie *Grease*.

Five Star are a group who have made smart casual wear popular.

body, allowing greater ease of movement for active women. Flat, boyish figures became fashionable, and women wore special corsets to hide their natural shape. Clothing became loose, often with no waist or a loose gathered bodice. The military look was introduced, with deep pockets, belts and high, stand-up collars.

Male fashion did not change very much, although styles did become simpler and more functional, with greater emphasis on comfort. In 1916 the jumper was introduced, indicating the increasingly casual approach to clothes.

1916 — Costume of brown serge — black velvet & stitched trimming — felt hat in brown & red — feather — gloves — fur muff — white blouse — gaiters — black shoes.

1914 — afternoon dress

The Industrial Revolution

The development of power-driven textile machinery in the late eighteenth and early nineteenth centuries completely changed the textile industry. For this reason the period is known as the Industrial Revolution. Both the

Textile production during the Industrial Revolution. What hardships did workers suffer?

method and speed of textile production were radically altered — suddenly, better-quality cloth could be produced much faster than by traditional methods.

As a result of faster production, cost was lowered, and mass production of reasonably priced fabric meant that more people could afford to buy more clothes. This demand for clothing has led to the development of a fashion industry that constantly strives to keep up our interest by introducing new clothing fashions.

Social problems were caused at the beginning of the Industrial Revolution, as many people lost their jobs to the new machines. *Cottage industry* ceased to be profitable. Eventually, however, the increased demand for textiles resulted in more jobs, and people were once again employed.

Activity

(1) Find out who invented the spinning jenny and what this invention did.
(2) Find a picture of or draw a spinning jenny, labelling the main parts.
(3) What were the advantages of a spinning jenny?

Fashion designers and fashion houses

Fashion designers have become increasingly popular and influential during the present century. A fashion designer usually works for a fashion house, which may produce two types of clothing:

- *Haute couture* — exclusive fashion, beautiful and creative in design, aimed at the wealthy, who can afford original, 'one-off' designs.
- *Prêt à porter* — 'ready to wear' clothes, the kind that most of us buy.

The main fashion houses are in Paris, London, Rome, Florence and New York. France has led the fashion industry since the seventeenth century, and its fashion houses date back to the middle of the nineteenth century.

Today, the fashion industry is very competitive. Japan has recently begun to make its mark, particularly through the work of designer Issey Miyake.

Twice a year, in January and July, the fashion houses present their collections. After months of work their ideas are presented to the public to accept or reject. In 1947 Dior designed the 'New Look', a change in hemlines that the public readily accepted. His fashion idea was therefore a success.

Designers who have achieved fame include Dior, Chanel, Saint-Laurent, Courrèges, Schiaparelli, Valentino, Nina Ricci and Worth. More recent designers of note include Claude Montana, Sonia Rykiel and Issey Miyake.

Nina Ricci Design

Karl Langerfeld design for Chanel

Courrèges design

Marc Bohan design for Dior

Yves St Laurent design

Activity

(1) In groups or individually, choose a fashion designer and research his or her background and the styles he or she is known for.
(2) Write up your information in a page or two, and include illustrations.

Revision questions

(1) Give three major reasons why people wear clothes.
(2) Explain why an astronaut needs special clothing.
(3) What are roles? Give three examples of different roles you play in an average month.
(4) Why has royalty become less important as a leader of fashion?
(5) Name four things that have had a major influence on fashion changes.
(6) Why did the First World War change the direction of fashion?
(7) How did the Industrial Revolution increase production? What effect did it have on the textile industry?
(8) What is the difference between *haute couture* and *prêt à porter*?

(9) Why has Paris remained a prominent fashion leader?

(10) What is the advantage of showing a fashion collection to the public at large?

Extension activity 1

The following terms were used in this chapter. See if you can unravel the letters to identify the words. The first word is done. The first letter of each word is underlined.

e.g. IANOLTRADI<u>T</u>   TRADITIONAL

<u>P</u>ROECIONTT   <u>R</u>EVOLIONUT
OS<u>M</u>MLE   <u>O</u>RECH
<u>C</u>ICRISATATNOI   TT<u>C</u>OAGE
<u>R</u>OSEL   <u>D</u>ENERSIG

Extension activity 2

(1) Research the clothing worn during one of the following periods in England: Plantagenet, Tudor, Victorian, Edwardian.

(2) Explain how the social position of people in this period affected their dress.

(3) What are the main differences between the clothing of that time and that developed during the First World War?

Glossary

Traditional dress — Passed down from generation to generation; not worn every day in most Westernised societies.

Ceremonial dress — Worn on special occasions, such as weddings, graduation ceremonies and by judges in court.

Cottage industry — Manufacturing or processing work, such as spinning and weaving, carried out in the home for a third party, who supplies the materials.

Ochre — Brownish yellow; the colour of a form of ferric oxide that occurs in nature and is used as a pigment.

Further reading

Anderson Black, J., Garland, M., and Kennett, F. *A History of Fashion*, St Michael, 1981

Bond, D. *The Guinness Guide to Twentieth Century Fashion*, Guinness Superlatives Ltd, 1981

Kennett, F. *Secrets of the Couturiers*, Orbis, 1984

2

Culture, dress and the textile arts

Dress and textiles have developed over many centuries to become part of the culture of different societies. Nowadays the people of many countries have adopted Western dress for everyday wear, but they still wear their traditional clothing with pride on special occasions.

In this chapter, we shall look at some cultural aspects of a number of countries in relation to traditional dress: the natural fibres used for clothing and traditional methods of producing or decorating cloth.

Peru

Traditional Peruvian clothing is still worn by tribespeople in the Andes mountains, most of whom are farmers or craftspeople. Their main form of clothing is a *poncho* made from llama or alpaca wool. The poncho covers the upper part of the body and consists of a large square of woven fabric with a central hole for the head.

Llama, alpaca, goats and sheep are kept as herd animals for wool. Llama and alpaca produce a longer, thicker fibre than sheep, resulting in a coarser cloth. The colourful llama fleeces produce interesting shades of browns and creams.

The people weave cloth from handspun yarn and make embroideries depicting stories or local customs, using dyed or natural-coloured threads of llama wool.

The shepherds who tend sheep and llama in the mountains spend much of their time spinning yarn with a *drop spindle* or *distaff and*

Country	Fibre	Method of production	Decoration
Peru	Wool	Drop spinning	
China	Silk	From silkworms	
India	Cotton	Wheel spinning	
New Zealand	Flax	From flax plant	
Japan	Silk and cotton		Stencil printing and screen printing
Indonesia	Cotton		Batik dyeing

Hand-spun alpaca yarn is woven to form a fabric for this Peruvian embroidery.

spindle. Fibres are drawn out with one hand and twisted onto a spinning stick with a heavy base made of wood or clay.

Wool is the best fibre for spinning because of its natural *crimp*, long *staple* and *oiliness*. The *crimp* is the waviness of the fibre. *Staple* refers to a bunch of fibres, the best length for a staple for hand spinning being 10–16 cm. The *oiliness* comes from *lanolin*, the natural grease in wool, which helps the fibres to cling together.

Spinning with a hand spindle is a slow operation. After only a few centimetres have been spun, the yarn is rolled onto the stick and retied before spinning can begin again.

Activity — Drop spinning

Wool should be combed or carded before it is spun.

Combing

Use a wide-toothed steel comb or a dog's comb. Hold the staple between the fingers and thumb of one hand, and comb the outermost tips first. Then take hold of the tips, and comb the other end. Don't comb the middle section. Place the combed staples in a basket, with the tips pointing the same way.

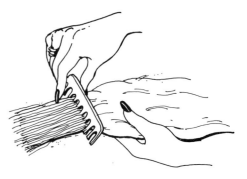

Carding

Using a set of hand carders, place a staple on the left-hand card. Draw the right card across the lower edge of the left-hand card. A fringe of wool will develop. Place the right card half-way on the left card, and comb gently downwards. Comb the whole length of the staple. The wool should not be on the right card. Place the wool on the left card, and comb the whole length of the staple. Flip onto the back of the card, and roll lightly to make a *rolag*.

(1) Draw out fibres between the thumb and forefinger of each hand.

The top card is stroked across the lower one.

The fibre is rolled by hand into a rolag.

The three processes of hand spinning are:

- Forming a thread by drawing out fibres.
- Adding strength by twisting fibres to make a yarn.
- Winding the yarn onto a bobbin.

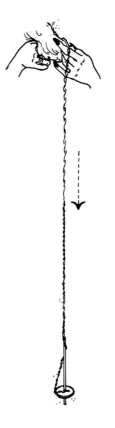

(2) Continue drawing out and spinning until the spindle reaches the floor.

(3) Twist the spindle with the left hand.

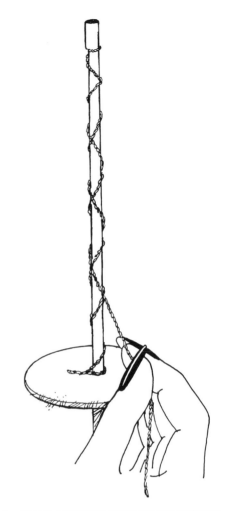

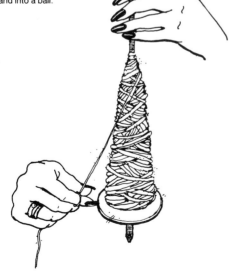

(5) When the spindle is full, wind the wool off and into a ball.

(4) Undo the slip knot, and wind the yarn up along the shaft of the spindle.

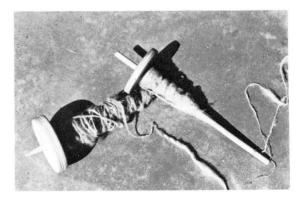

Drop spindles containing woollen yarn

Wool

Wool is a protein fibre. It contains the protein *keratin*, which is also found in human hair.

Wool is easily identified under the microscope. The longitudinal section of the fibre shows scales.

Notice the overlapping scales. They look like a stack of paper cups. Try feeling the rough scales on a strand of human hair. Which way do the scales on your hair run — towards the scalp or the ends?

These overlapping scales may cause wool fibres to *felt* or shrink. Wool fibres sometimes felt when they are agitated, particularly when they are washed. The diagram shows the catching effect of projecting scales when they are agitated. This is called the *directional frictional effect* (DFE).

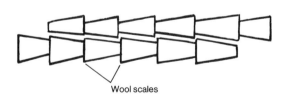

Wool scales

To prevent shrinkage or felting caused by the DFE, wool fibres can be covered with a resin, so that the scales do not project. Another method is to bond a wool fibre with resin, so that bridges of resin link the fibres and prevent them from rubbing against one another.

Producing woollen yarns

There are seven main stages involved in producing woollen yarns.

(1) *Sorting*

When sheep are shorn, the wool is classed according to the length and quality of fibres.

(2) *Scouring*

Dirt and vegetable matter collected in the fleece is removed by washing in warm soapy water. The wool grease, *lanolin*, is also removed.

(3) *Carbonisation*

Any burrs in the wool are removed by treating the wool with weak sulphuric acid. The acid breaks down the cellulose structure of the burr, allowing it to be crushed and removed.

(4) *Carding*

Wool is next fed into rotating rollers containing wire brushes. This process aligns the fibres, so that they lie parallel to each other.

Carding also separates short fibres from long fibres. The short fibres are used to make *woollen yarn*. The long fibres make a better-quality *worsted yarn* (see stage 6).

(5) *Combing*

The long fibres used to make worsted yarn are *combed*. This process involves passing the rope of carded wool through steel combs on a roller to remove any short fibres.

(6) *Spinning*

The rope or *sliver* of wool fibres is drawn out thinly and then twisted. Woollen yarn is soft and lightly twisted, while worsted yarn is fine and tightly twisted. The yarns are then wound onto *bobbins*, which look like cotton reels, ready for weaving or knitting.

(7) *Plying*

Two or more yarns may be twisted together, or *plyed*, to give them more strength; for example 8 ply wool contains eight yarns of a standard thickness spun together.

Wool count

The thickness of a wool fibre is described as its *count*. A coarse or thick fibre has a low count, while a fine wool has a high count. A superfine merino wool may have a count of 80. A thick rug wool may have a count of 30–40.

Properties of wool

- Wool is *elastic* and *crease resistant*. The natural crimp of wool makes it behave like a spring. Because wool can stretch and return to its original shape, woollen fabrics are crease resistant.
- Wool is a *warm* fibre. It takes up more moisture from the air than any other fibre and can absorb about one-third of its own weight of water without feeling wet. Heat is generated while the moisture is being absorbed.
- Wool *felts* easily if placed in hot water or agitated. For this reason it should be washed very carefully by hand in warm water, using a mild detergent. Wool is deliberately shrunk in hot water to produce felt fabrics, which are used for craft work, hats and carpet underlay.
- Wool does not *burn* readily and is therefore recommended for children's wear, toys, rugs and nightwear.
- Wool may be attacked by *moths* if it is not aired regularly.

To store woollen garments, wash them, dry them well and place them in clean plastic bags. Seal the bags well to prevent attack by moths.

The Woolmark symbol

In 1964, the International Wool Secretariat introduced this trademark to identify products made of pure wool. Today, the Woolmark symbol is also used on woollen fabrics and yarns containing up to 5 per cent of other fibres.

Certification Trade Mark
Pure new wool

The Woolmark

The Woolblend mark

This symbol was introduced in 1971 to identify yarns and fabrics blended from wool and other fibres. Underneath the symbol, the percentage of wool and other fibres in the fabric must be stated.

Certification Trade Mark
Wool rich blend

The Woolblend mark

Activity

Find labels from clothes and furnishings which show either the Woolmark or Woolblend symbol. Can you find any variations on these labels?

China

To the Chinese, worship of ancestors is very important, and much emphasis is placed on spiritual idealism. The Chinese believed that their society was superior to all others and did not approve of the machine age, believing that machines would produce poor-quality goods. They did not change their methods of garment production with the machine age, and cottage industry is still important in China. Many Western countries import Chinese hand-sewn garments, particularly heavily embroidered blouses and tablecloths.

The Chinese developed the *kimono*, which was later adopted by the Japanese.

In 1911 a revolution began in China that ended in 1949 with the Communists in power under Mao Tse-tung. Traditional Chinese dress was abandoned, and cheaper, mass-produced clothing was made available to all. Both men and women wore a similar uniform, consisting of baggy trousers and workshirts made of cotton. Winter clothes were made of padded cotton for warmth. Cotton was chosen, because wool was not widely available and silk was too expensive.

Before the Communist revolution, a variety of fabrics had been used for clothing, including silk, satin and velvet, as well as gauze and cotton in summer.

The north-eastern part of China is very cold in winter. To provide warmth, clothes were padded with wool or silk, or layers of clothes were worn. The layers often consisted of clothes of similar cut and length.

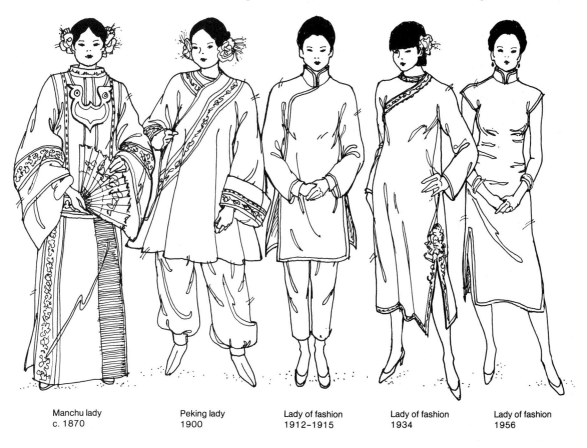

| Manchu lady c. 1870 | Peking lady 1900 | Lady of fashion 1912–1915 | Lady of fashion 1934 | Lady of fashion 1956 |

What features of Chinese women's dress have been retained over the past 100 years?

| Chinese official c. 1850 | Government official late 19th century | 20th century | Men's formal dress 1911–1949 | Military dress 1936 |

How has Chinese menswear become more functional since 1850?

Trousers, worn by both males and females, were fastened around the waist by a soft girdle.

Symbols were used on clothing and served two functions:

- To confirm virtues of or good omens for the wearer.
- To show official rank or social position.

The best-known symbol is the *dragon*, which represented imperial power. Other symbols included the *phoenix*, which represented peace and prosperity, and the *unicorn*, which represented grandeur and wise administration. The king of beasts in China is the *tiger*, which represented valour.

Colours also had special meanings for the Chinese. Black, white, yellow, red and green represented the five elements, water, metal, earth, fire and wood. Yellow was the central colour, representing earth and the centre of the universe as dominated by the Emperor, and was therefore the colour worn by the imperial family.

Activity

Find out the answers to the following questions and report your findings to the class next lesson.

(1) Why did Chinese women have their feet bound?
(2) What changes are occurring in Chinese fashion today?

Silk

Silk is produced by the larvae of the silk moth. Silk fibres are exceptionally long and are called *filaments*. The protein *fibroin* is found in silk. This differs from the keratin in wool in that it does not contain the chemical sulphur.

A longitudinal view of silk under the microscope shows a soft, fine, lustrous, smooth, round fibre.

The silk moth lays eggs, from which *larvae* hatch. The larvae feed on mulberry leaves and grow into silkworms. When the silkworms mature, they spin cocoons of silk and enclose themselves. After a time, the worm changes to a moth and escapes the cocoon.

Silk worm larvae

Producing silk yarns

There are four processes involved in making silk yarns.

(1) *Degumming*

Cocoons are sorted according to size, colour and condition. They are then placed in hot soapy water to remove the gum that sticks the silk filaments together.

(2) *Reeling*

The filaments are wound onto a bobbin.

(3) *Twisting*

The filaments are then *twisted*, in order to make them stronger.

Silk filaments being twisted onto bobbins

4) *Weighting*

Owing to the loss of weight that occurs in the degumming process, tin salts are added to increase the weight of silk according to what it is to be used for. Japanese silks used for scarves have very little or no weighting, whereas silk taffeta for a ball gown or a man's tie may have up to 25 per cent weighting.

Properties of silk

• Silk has some elasticity, which makes it comfortable to wear and fairly *crease resistant*.

Its ability to resist creasing depends on the weave, the amount of weighting and the treatment.

- Silk *absorbs moisture* readily, which makes it comfortable to wear.
- As it is a *poor conductor* of heat, silk feels warm to touch and wear.
- Silk is resistant to mildew. It is also resistant to moths if it is clean.
- Silk can be blended with wool fibres to produce a fabric that *resists shrinkage* when washed.

A mild soap should be used when washing silk to prevent the fabric from yellowing. It is also a good idea to roll it in a towel and to iron it while still damp, as drying in the air also causes silk to yellow.

Fabrics made from silk

Brocade

A thick fabric with a raised design produced on a *Jacquard loom* during weaving. Used for curtains, upholstery and evening wear.

Chiffon

A very thin fabric that drapes well, because the yarns are highly twisted. Used for blouses, scarves and evening dresses.

Georgette

A soft fabric with a dull surface, made from yarn that has alternating right and left twists.

Organza

A fine, transparent fabric that is very stiff and highly weighted.

Taffeta

A stiff fabric made from weighted silk. It rustles when worn and is used for men's ties and evening dresses. In 1981, when Lady Diana Spencer married Prince Charles, she chose silk taffeta for her wedding dress. Many fashion commentators felt that this fabric was a poor choice, as it crushes easily and does not hang or drape well. What do you think?

The Princess of Wales in her wedding dress

India

The earliest Indian garments were made from simple lengths of fabric, which were wrapped around the person rather than sewn. It was not until the eighth century that garments were sewn, a technique brought by Moslem invaders from North Africa.

Traditional Indian dress consists of a *sari* for women, while men wear loin cloths called *pachedis*, turbans and shawls. Until synthetic fibres were developed, most garments were made of cotton.

The technique of spinning with a simple spinning wheel was invented in India. Simple wheels were first made with bamboo strips and a string driving band.

Mahatma Gandhi, the famous Indian spiritual and political leader this century, reintroduced hand spinning to the Indian people as a method of producing yarn to make cotton cloth. The uneven, hand-spun yarn makes a textured cloth that is much sought after in countries like England for furnishing fabrics.

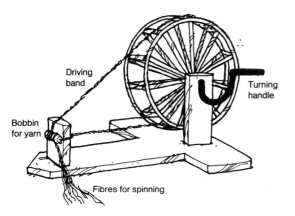

Driving band

Turning handle

Bobbin for yarn

Fibres for spinning

A simple hand-operated spinning wheel

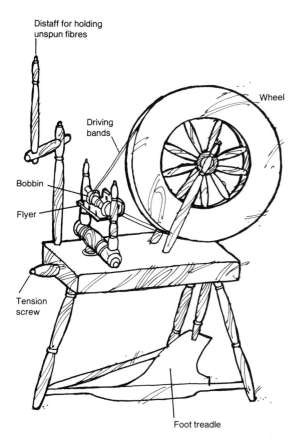

Distaff for holding unspun fibres

Wheel

Driving bands

Bobbin

Flyer

Tension screw

Foot treadle

A foot-treadle spinning wheel

Wool is easier to spin on a spinning wheel than cotton, because it has a natural crimp that binds fibres together and a relatively long staple length. Cotton fibres are often dampened with water to help hold them together while spinning.

A spinning wheel is really a drop spindle placed horizontally, with a drive band added to make it revolve faster.

Activity — Spinning cotton with a spinning wheel

Learning to spin on a wheel is simply a matter of practice. Before you begin to spin, study the wheel and work out what function each part has.

(1) First, treadle your wheel to get the feel of the spinning motion. The treadling action should not be fast but just enough to keep the wheel going around steadily. You should practise this movement until it becomes automatic.

(2) Tie a length of spun yarn onto the bobbin. Draw this yarn around one of the hooks on the *orifice*. Then comb or card some wool or cotton.

(3) With your right hand, turn the wheel clockwise, and begin to treadle. Allow the combed fibres to attach themselves to the tied yarn. Use your right hand to draw fibres away from you and your left hand to hold and regulate the amount of twist.

(4) Allow the yarn to feed onto the bobbin when twisted. Too much twist will break the yarn. If the yarn is feeding onto the bobbin too quickly, loosen the tension on the bobbin.

(5) When you first begin to use a spinning wheel, have a friend help you in case the treadle stops or reverses. Sometimes it takes a while for your foot and hand action to become co-ordinated.

Cotton

Cotton is grown in warm, moist climates such as the southern states of North America, Egypt, the West Indies and India. It is also produced on the west coast of Africa, and in Uganda, China and Russia.

Cotton consists of *cellulose*, which forms the walls of all plant cells. A longitudinal view of a cotton fibre under the microscope shows a long, tube-like structure with gentle *convolutions* or twists. In a cross-section, the fibre appears kidney shaped.

Cotton fibre under a microscope

In 1844, John Mercer observed that cotton fibres swelled when immersed in a bath of water and caustic soda. This process, called *mercerisation*, makes cotton fibres stronger, more lustrous and able to accept dye easily.

Check the labels of cotton sewing thread. Why do you think it is mercerised?

Producing cotton yarn

There are six processes involved in producing cotton yarn.

(1) *Harvesting*

Cotton fibres are taken from the seed or *boll* of the cotton plant.

(2) *Ginning*

The fibres are separated from the seeds in the boll.

(3) *Cleaning*

The fibres are cleaned and formed into a *lap*, like a roll of cotton wool.

(4) *Carding*

Wire-toothed rollers straighten the fibres and form them into a thick rope called a *sliver*.

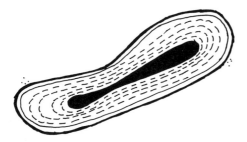

Cross-section of a cotton fibre before mercerisation. Notice the kidney shape.

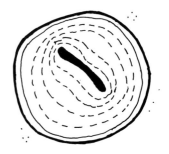

Cross-section of a cotton fibre after mercerisation. Notice the swollen fibre.

(5) *Drawing*

The sliver is drawn and twisted to make a thinner rope called a *roving*.

(6) *Spinning*

The spinning frame twists the roving many times to make a strong, thin yarn, which threads onto a bobbin.

Properties of cotton

- Cotton *absorbs moisture* and is a *good conductor* of heat.
- Cotton is a relatively inexpensive textile.
- When blended with polyester, cotton resists creasing and wrinkling. The resulting fabric is often labelled as drip-dry, non-iron.
- As a fibre by itself, cotton creases easily and needs frequent ironing.
- Cotton is stronger when wet than dry, so it can withstand frequent washing and hot water. This makes it a *durable* fibre, suitable for such uses as overalls, sheets, uniforms and sewing thread.
- Cotton is attacked by *mildew* but not moths.
- Sunlight *yellows* and eventually *rots* cotton.
- Cotton tears easily, because it is inelastic.
- Cotton does not accumulate static electricity.

Cotton is one of the fibres most used for clothing throughout the world. It is becoming more important as a blend with wool, nylon, polyester, linen and rayon. Viyella is the trade name of a product containing 55 per cent wool and 45 per cent cotton. Clydella contains 20 per cent wool and 80 per cent cotton. These fabrics are used for shirts and dresses and are often cheaper than pure wool products.

Activity

Check the label of your school shirt or summer uniform. What fibres does it contain?

Why do you think the manufacturer chose these fibres for a uniform?

New Zealand

The country of origin of the Maori people is still the subject of debate. It is agreed that they are a Polynesian race, which migrated towards the rising sun. An adventurous, seafaring people, they were forced to migrate because of overpopulation and war.

The Polynesian social system is based on the family. Within each tribe there were two main groups, each with a special rank. The chief rank was known as *rangatira*, and the commoners were known as *ware* and *tutua*. There was also a third group, known as *tuhunga*, consisting of priests and highly skilled craft workers.

The Maoris traditionally used flax for their ceremonial dress, which for women consists of a grass (flax) skirt and an embroidered bodice and for men consists of a wrap cloth.

Maori women making flax skirts

Maori designs are rich and colourful, decorated with earth colours and cross-stitch. The cross-stitch is often done in wool, in colours of red, white and black.

Flax

Flax is the plant that produces the linen fibre and is the oldest plant fibre used by humans to produce fabric. Egyptian mummies were wrapped in linen. These linen wrappings can still be seen intact in museums, because linen is such a durable fibre. Today, linen has largely been replaced by the less expensive man-made fibres such as nylon, especially for such things as ropes, sails, fishing lines and nets. Nylon is as strong and durable as linen but is cheaper to produce.

Under a microscope, linen looks like bamboo, having crosswise joints called *nodes*. The cells are held in bundles by a pectin wax. These long, strong fibres make linen fabric inelastic, and it therefore crushes easily.

Producing linen yarn

There are six stages involved in producing linen yarn.

(1) *Harvesting*

The roots and plant are both extracted from the ground by a harvester.

(2) *Retting*

The stems are soaked, so that they decompose (or rot). This process may be carried out in the field or factory.

(3) *Scutching*

The decomposed stems are crushed and beaten by rollers. The fibre bundles left behind are called *tow*.

(4) *Hacking*

Short fibres are removed by brushing. The long fibres left behind are formed into long rope-like sliver by barbed roller brushes.

(5) *Carding*

The fibres are aligned by means of wire-toothed rollers.

(6) *Spinning*

The sliver is twisted and drawn out to make a fine, strong yarn.

Properties of linen

- Linen is expensive compared to similar man-made fabrics such as nylon and rayon.
- Linen washes easily.
- Linen crushes easily and needs to be ironed with a hot iron.

Japan

Japan is a nation of islands on the fringe of the Asian continent. The Japanese are a Mongolian people. It is thought that the area was settled by people from China as well as from Mongolia and Siberia.

The Japanese adopted the Chinese *kimono* and wore it as an undergarment. The kimono is loose and is therefore comfortable to wear in humid climates. Over the years there has been little change in the kimono. A simple garment, it consist of strips of fabric sewn together, with some shaping in the collar, lapel and sleeves. The stitching is removed before washing.

Getting dressed can be time consuming for a Japanese woman, who traditionally wears:

- Long cotton undergarment
- Kimono, kept in place by a thin belt
- A sash (*obi*) bound around the waist over the kimono
- To improve the finished look, a padded sash called an *obi-age* and a cord-like tie called an *obi-dome*, which goes over the *obi-age*.

Although silks, gauze and brocades were being produced in China from 646 B.C., early Japanese cloth was mostly made from hemp, ramie mulberry and wisteria vine. Silk was not known in Japan until the second century and became a highly prized fibre, costly and time consuming to produce. Silk and cotton were the main fibres used for making fabric for kimonos.

The Japanese liked to decorate cloth to indicate class differences and family groups. Kimonos were sometimes decorated with exquisite embroideries. Highly prized yarns for this purpose included gold and silver threads. Gems, too, were often used to decorate cloth.

Batik and *stencil dyeing* were early methods used to decorate cloth. *Resist dyeing*, using a rice paste, and *tie dyeing* were much later processes. *Block printing*, a cheaper form of decoration, was used by the poorer people.

Weaving and embroidery were the major methods of producing and decorating cloth. The first real brocade fabric was made in Japan.

Natural dyes from plants were used to colour fabrics. Safflowers, for example, produced attractive tones of yellow.

Japanese children wearing traditional kimonos

Activity

For this activity you will need a piece of plain cotton fabric and a piece of paper, each measuring 30 cm × 20 cm.

(1) Using a ruler, draw the kimono on your paper as illustrated. Draw the front and back. Curve the corners.
(2) Cut out your paper pattern, and label it with the symbols used on commercial patterns.
(3) Pin your paper pattern to the fabric, and cut around it.
(4) Remove the pattern. Using a small running stitch, sew the side-seams and sleeve seams.
(5) Paste the completed kimono into your workbook.

Stencil printing

Stencil printing was developed by the Japanese. A design is first cut from a sheet of paper and coated with oil, wax or varnish to protect it. A separate stencil is needed for each colour required. To obtain a perfect print, the stencils must register with each other.

Screen printing

A further development in fabric decoration occurred with *screen printing*. It is believed to have developed from *stencil printing* and makes use of frames, which were originally covered with silk. Nowadays screen-printing frames are covered with nylon or polyester, as silk is too expensive.

Screen printing was originally developed as a method of adding decoration to the surface of fabric. The process has several disadvantages for manufacturers. First, because it is done by hand, it is a slow process. Second, limited length is produced, because it takes so much time. Third, each screen can be used for only one colour, so in a complicated design using five colours, five screens are required for each section.

For the person who wishes to create individual designs, however, the method provides scope for design while giving precise detail.

The screen originally consisted of a wooden frame with silk fabric stretched over it. Today, the frame is still wooden, but the fabric used is often nylon or polyester. The fabric mesh must be fine enough to allow the dyestuff to pass through to print the fabric.

The frame is laid on the fabric to be printed, the dye is placed at one edge of the frame, and a *squeegee* moves across the screen, forcing the dye through the open areas onto the fabric.

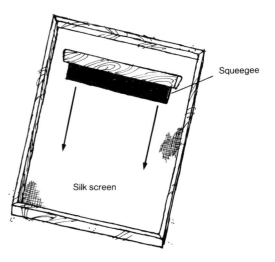

Squeegee

Silk screen

Activity — Making a screen-printed shoulder bag

You will need

- Thick drawing paper 30 cm × 30 cm
- As many screens as you require colours, 30 cm × 30 cm
- As many squeegees as you require colours
- Newspaper
- Sharp scissors or Stanley knife
- A piece of wood 30 cm × 30 cm to rest your paper on while cutting out
- 1 m of unbleached calico
- Printing paste (dyestuff)
- Metal spoon

Method

(1) Decide on a design for your bag. Children's colouring books with large drawings provide good ideas. Make sure that you use heavy, sharp. pencil lines when you draw the design. on your paper.

(2) On each section of the design, write the colour you wish to use (see diagram).

(3) Cut out the areas of the design that are to be printed. Where two or more colours are being used, the pieces cut out need to be saved, so that they can be placed over the previously printed sections to prevent the next colour reprinting the previous one.

(4) Cut the calico into two pieces measuring 40 cm × 90 cm, leaving an 18 cm × 90 cm strip for the handle.

(5) Cover your table with plenty of newspaper.

(6) Fold one of the pieces of calico in half, and lay it flat on the table. Place the paper with the cut-out design in the centre of the calico.

(7) Place the screen on top of the design, ensuring that the paper overhangs on all four sides of the screen.

(8) Place one to three tablespoons of printing paste on the top end of the screen. The amount of printing paste used depends on the size of the part of the design to be covered.

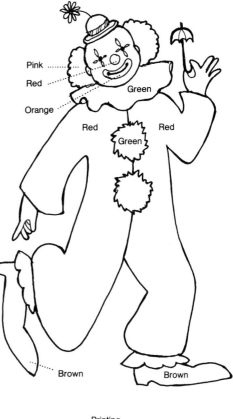

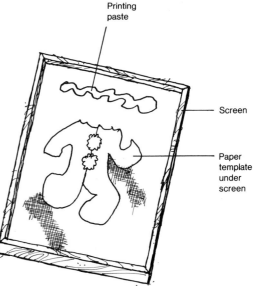

(9) Have someone hold the screen still while you squeegee the printing paste down to the part of the screen nearest to you.

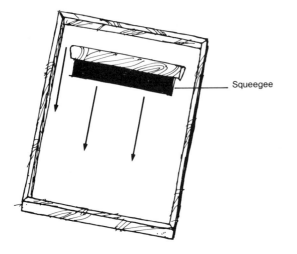

Squeegee

(10) Lift off the screen gently. Empty leftover printing paste into a container. Wash the screen and squeegee immediately in cold running water to remove any paste. Dry screens thoroughly.

(11) If more than one colour is required, leave the first colour to dry for two to three hours, then apply the next colour. Remember to cover parts that have already been coloured, and cut out new parts of the design you want coloured.

(12) Outline your screen printing with crewel embroidery for interesting textural effects.

(13) Iron the print to set the colour, so that it does not run when washed.

(14) Make up the bag by sewing the side-seams of the printed part as well as the lining. Join the lining to the bag at the top, machining in the strap with a double row of stitching for strength.

After screen printing, embroider to complete the picture.

The completed bag

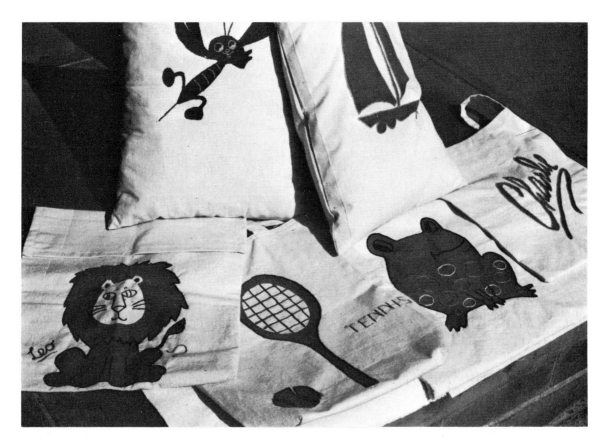

Bags and pillows can be screen printed with one or many colours. By adding embroidery, single-template designs can be made to look just as interesting as the multi-template clown.

Indonesia

Indonesia is situated at the crossroads of ocean trade. Over the centuries it has been influenced by India, China, Europe and the Islamic world.

The textiles produced in Indonesia can be divided into three groups.

Ikat

The word *ikat* means to tie or bind. Yarns are bound or wrapped and then dyed. The weaver must know the pattern, so that the fabric is dyed only where colour is required. Each district has its own ikat pattern.

Silk weaving and songket work

This technique was inspired by Islamic traders, who brought gold, silver and silk threads. Silk weaving was often used in making *sarongs*.

Batik

Batik is a method of adding design and colour to woven fabric. It is mainly done in central Java and has been in use for many hundreds of years. A bamboo and copper vessel called a *tjanting* is filled with hot beeswax. The wax is then applied to the fabric in the chosen design. (The method is described more fully in the activity on page 34.)

Each tribe had its own batik design, the most widely used designs being geometrical. Indonesians judge the quality of batik by comparing the front and back of the fabric. If the batik is the same on both sides, it is considered to be of excellent quality.

Activity — Making a batik scarf

You will need
- Fine cotton fabric (washed and ironed) 50 cm × 50 cm
- Wax — a white candle is suitable, but beeswax is preferable
- Saucepan to heat wax
- Paint brush
- Cold water dye

Method
(1) Draw your design on paper, and place it under the fabric. Pin to prevent the pattern from moving.
(2) Using liquid wax, cover the areas of the design you wish to be kept white.
(3) Place the fabric in a dye bath.
(4) Rinse off excess dye in cold water. Dry fabric.
(5) Repeat the process if you wish to use another colour.

(6) When your design is complete, remove the wax by placing the fabric between two sheets of brown paper and ironing with a warm iron.
(7) Roll hems required on four sides and slip stitch.
(8) Finally, wash in cold water, dry and press.

Words to remember

fibre	filament
carding	conductor
combing	shrinkage
woollen	chiffon
scouring	taffeta
carbonisation	organza
microscopic	Jacquard
fictional	convolution
lanolin	lap
worsted	ginning
sliver	boll
scutching	roving
bobbin	absorb
plying	Clydella
crease resistant	Viyella
mildew	nodes
felt	pectin
elasticity	retting
mercerisation	tow
degumming	squeegee
fibroin	screen
cellulose	template
keratin	design
cocoon	calico
weighting	

Revision exercises

(1) Jute and hemp are other plant fibres used to make textiles. Find out what they are used for, and paste a sample of each in your workbook.

(2) Camel, angora, mohair and alpaca are other animal fibres used for textiles. Why are they relatively expensive compared to wool? See if you can find some of these fibres, and paste them in your book.

(3) Using a map of the world, mark in the major cotton-, wool-, silk- and flax-growing areas in different colours. Include a key to indicate what each colour represents.

(4) Here is a list of fabric names. Next to each, write the fibre it is made from.

poplin_____
tweed_____
flannel_____
georgette_____
linen_____
flannelette_____
lawn_____

(5) Find clothing labels for cotton and polyester and wool and polyester fabrics. Copy the labels into your book, showing the percentage of each fibre used in each case.

(6) Take two pieces of woollen fabric of the same size and shape. Wash one piece gently by hand in a mild detergent in warm water. Wash the other piece with a strong detergent and agitate in boiling water.

Compare the fabrics after washing. Now draw up a list of rules to remember when washing woollen garments.

Further reading

Dixon, M. *The Wool Book*, Hamlyn, London, 1979

Gostelow, M. *Embroidery: Traditional Designs from All Over the World*, Cavendish House, London, 1982

Konieczny, M.G. *Textiles of Baluchistan*, British Museum Publications, London, 1979

Leadbeater, E. *Spinning and Spinning Wheels*, Shire Publications, Aylesbury, 1979

Sutton, A. *The Structure of Weaving*, Batsford, 1982

3

Decoration of fabrics

Dyeing

Natural dyes

The first colours used to dye fabrics were obtained from animal and vegetable sources. Sepia brown was obtained from cuttlefish, green from mosses and lichens, cochineal pink from a South American beetle, browns and blacks from logwood bark, and yellow from flowers such as saffron and marigolds. Many varieties of colours can be obtained from such natural dyes, but these colours are not very *colourfast*. They fade in sunlight and wash out. Because they are difficult to collect, they are also uneconomical for dyeing large amounts of fabric.

Today, natural dyes are used for craft work and in dyeing handspun wool. Wool absorbs dyes easily, whereas many other fibres such as nylon and polyester do not. *Mordants* allow dyes to be taken up readily by fibres and are placed in the dye bath before dyeing takes place. The most common chemicals used for mordanting are: alum, chrome, iron and tin.

Activity — Dyeing with natural dyes

You will need
- Pair of rubber gloves
- Old saucepans or large beakers
- Dyestuff — can be any plant, bark, fruit, flower, leaf or stem
- Mordants — any of the following, which can be bought at a pharmacy: chrome, tin, alum, cream of tartar, ferrous sulphate, copper sulphate, acetic acid (vinegar)
- Bunsen burners and tripods or hot plates
- Hand-spun wool that has been washed in a mild detergent
- Bucket to collect and store dyestuffs
- Teaspoon measure

Method
(1) Collect dyestuff. Use the guide to natural dyes on p. 38 for colour ideas.
(2) Place the dyestuff in a saucepan or beaker with the same volume of water and bring to the boil. Boil until a good colour is obtained in the water. Some dyestuffs, such as woody plants, which do not readily make a paste with water, are best soaked overnight before boiling.
(3) Drain off the dye into another saucepan. Add the mordant of your choice and dissolve with a spoon. Use 1 teaspoon of mordant to each 200 ml dye.
(4) Add damp wool and bring to the boil slowly. *Do not stir*, as agitation will felt the wool.
(5) Simmer for fifteen minutes.
(6) Rinse thoroughly and hang out to dry.

Results

Make up a sample page of natural dyes in your workbook, copying the following chart:

Wool sample	Dyestuff	Mordant used	Colour of wool

Conclusion

(1) List the disadvantages of dyeing with natural dyes.
(2) What are natural dyes mainly used for today?
(3) Place some of your wool samples in the sunlight and record any changes that take place over one or two days.

Guide to natural dyes

Dyestuff	Mordant	Colour
Blackberry shoots	Iron sulphate	Black
Camomile	Alum	Bright yellow
Walnut shell	Alum or any mordant	Brown
Seaweed	Alum or any mordant	Brown
Onion skins	Alum or chrome	Gold
Mulberries	Tannic acid	Dusty pink
Mulberries	Cream of tartar	Tan
Dahlia flowers	Alum	Bright orange
Madder	Alum	Red
Privet leaves	Alum	Lemon/green
Privet leaves	Copper sulphate	Emerald green
Marigold flowers	Alum	Brown/green
Red cabbage	Chrome	Aqua
Bracken	Alum	Yellow
Mushrooms	Alum	Grey
Blackberries	Acetic acid	Mauve
Carrot tops	Alum	Green
Parsley	Chrome	Green
Fennel	Alum	Bright yellow
Spinach	Cream of tartar	Olive green

Colourfastness

Dyes should not transfer from one fabric to another. Many cheap dyes and dark shades of dye rub off easily onto light-coloured fabrics. Test to see if a fabric is colourfast by rubbing it with a damp white cloth. If colour comes off on the white cloth, you will need to wash the garment separately from other clothes.

Methods of dyeing

Dyeing can be carried out at any stage in the manufacture of fabric. Fibres, yarns or fabrics may be dyed.

Stock or fibre dyeing

Loose fibres are dyed before spinning in a *vat* containing a *dye bath*. A dye bath is a dye dissolved in water. Most dyes require water temperatures near boiling point to penetrate the fibres well.

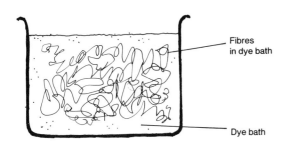

Fibres in dye bath

Dye bath

Yarn dyeing

Yarn wound onto bobbins or cones placed on perforated steel rods is lowered into the dye bath. Yarn dyeing is often used for fabrics with varying weave patterns or borders. Yarn-dyed fabrics usually look the same on both sides.

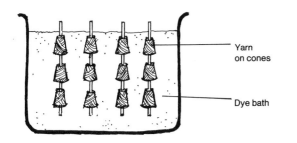

Yarn on cones

Dye bath

Piece dyeing

The whole length of fabric is made and then put through the dye bath. Dye cannot always penetrate to the fibres, however, and when the yarn is pulled out, the undyed section can sometimes be seen. Methods of piece dyeing include:

- *Jig dyeing*, where the fabric is rolled from one roller to another. The fabric goes through the dye bath and is then reversed until sufficient dye has been taken up.

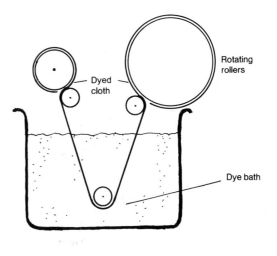

Rotating rollers

Dyed cloth

Dye bath

- *Pad stenter dyeing*, where the fabric is passed through a dye bath, and the dye is then forced into the fabric by pressure from *pad mangles*.

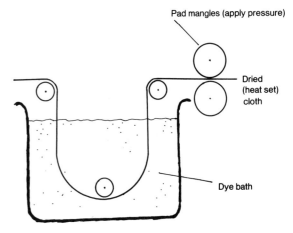

Pad mangles (apply pressure)

Dried (heat set) cloth

Dye bath

- *Pressure beam dyeing*, where fabric is wound onto a perforated beam, which is placed into a large pressure chamber. The dye bath runs through the fabric under heat and pressure in the sealed container. The small holes or perforations in the beam allow the dye to pass through the fabric.

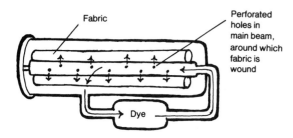

Properties of a good dye

- *Colourfastness* — Colours should not fade after repeated washing.
- *Lightfastness* — Colours should not fade in light (particularly important for curtains).
- *Insoluble in drycleaning fluids* — Dyes should not come out of the fabric in drycleaning liquids.
- *Perspiration fastness* — Dyes should not discolour with body perspiration.
- *Salt water and chlorine proof* — Particularly important for swimwear.

Synthetic dyes

In 1856 the first chemical aniline dyes were discovered. The first colour to be developed was mauve.

Types of synthetic dyes used today

- *Direct dyes* — Poor washfastness. Used mainly for cottons. Inexpensive.
- *Basic dyes* — Poor washfastness and lightfastness. Excellent colour range. Used for acrylics.
- *Azoic dyes* — Excellent washfastness and lightfastness. Used for cottons, linens and rayons.

- *Acid dyes* — Good washfastness and lightfastness. Used on protein fibres such as wool and silk, also on polyamides (nylon).
- *Sulphur dyes* — Give dull browns, blues, yellows, greens. Good washfastness.
- *Vat dyes* — Excellent washfastness and lightfastness. Used on cotton, linen and rayon. Relatively expensive, but give a large range of bright colours.
- *Dispense dyes* — Good washfastness and lightfastness. Used for nylon, polyester and acrylics.
- *Reactive dyes* — Good washfastness and lightfastness. Combine chemically with the fibre, so are held fast. Used for all natural fibres and nylon.

Activity — Washfastness of dyes

You will need

- 4 squares of inexpensive cotton, coloured fabric, each 7 cm × 7 cm (one to be used for comparison later)
- 3 squares of white cotton fabric, each 7 cm × 7 cm
- Thread
- Needle
- 4 beakers or saucepans
- 2 dry sponges
- Liquid laundry detergent
- Bleach
- 3 bunsen burners or hot plates on a stove
- 1 tablespoon measure

Method

(1) Sew a piece of white cotton fabric to each piece of coloured fabric, using a large tacking stitch.
(2) Fill each beaker or saucepan with 150 ml of warm water. Label the beakers from 1 to 4.
(3) In beaker 1, place one of the three samples and stir in 1 tablespoon of detergent.
(4) In beaker 2, place another sample and bring to the boil, then stir in 1 tablespoon of detergent.
(5) In beaker 3, place the third sample and

	Staining on white cotton	Colour of washing after 10 min	% fading on colour using grey scales
Warm water			
Boiling water, detergent			
Boiling water, detergent, bleach			

bring to the boil, then stir in 1 tablespoon of detergent and 2 tablespoons of bleach.
(6) Stir and boil beakers 2 to 4 for ten minutes.
(7) Blot each sample dry with a sponge.
(8) Unpick the tacking, and mark each sample with the beaker number.
(9) Compare the colour of each sample with the untreated sample.

Results

Draw up a table like the one above to record your results.

Gauge the percentage of fading by using a set of grey scales, which give the grades or tones of grey from white to black. Each drop in shade or tone represents a 10 per cent fading of the previous tone. If you do not have grey scales, use a scale from 1 to 10. A value of 10 means no fading, 8 or 9 a little fading, and 1 or 2 would be near white.

Conclusion

In your workbook, answer the following questions:

(1) What washing conditions caused the greatest loss of colour?
(2) Which method of washing coloured fabrics would you choose in order to *retain* colour?
(3) Why shouldn't you wash coloured and white clothes together?

Printing

Printing decorates the surface of fabric. Thickened dye is laid on the surface of the fabric to form a pattern. After printing, the fabric is heated by steaming to fix the *printing paste* in the fabric.

There are four main types of printing:

- Colour is applied directly by screens, rollers or blocks. This is called *direct printing*.
- The fabric is first printed with a mordant and then piece dyed. The only part of the dye that develops is the mordanted part. This is called *dyed printing*.
- A chemical is printed on part of the fabric to prevent the dye being absorbed. The fabric is then piece dyed, and only the non-treated part is printed. This is called *resist printing*. (It is the opposite to dyed printing.)
- Dyed plain fabric is printed with a bleach that removes colour in the printed areas. This is called *discharge printing*.

Block and screen printing are the most widely used methods of printing for craft work or original, limited, designer patterns. Both these methods were discussed in Chapter 2.

Roller printing

The design for the print is engraved on copper rollers. Each colour requires a separate roller. The rollers move over the fabric and continually feed printing paste from separate dye baths.

Transfer printing

This is the most recently developed method of printing. At present it is limited to fabrics that have at least 50 per cent polyester or polyam-

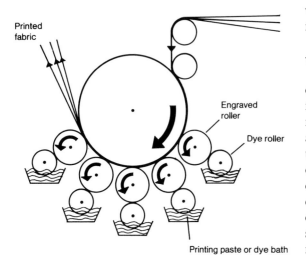

Roller printing

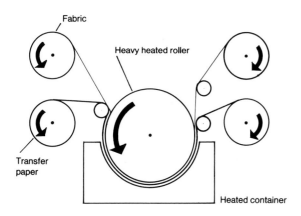

Transfer printing

ide fibres. The design is printed on a roll of paper, which is passed around a heavy, hot roller in contact with the fabric to be printed. At 200°C the dye changes from a solid to a liquid on the paper and back to a solid on the fabric. This process is called *sublimation*. It is a quick, clean method of printing.

Activity

Collect as many different samples of printed fabric as will fit easily on one page of your workbook. Label the type of printing or dyeing method used.

Words to remember

dye	lightfast
mordant	insoluble
natural	perspiration
alum	chlorine
tin	synthetic
chrome	direct
cuttlefish	basic
cochineal	azoic
colourstuff	sulphur
saffron	vat
marigold	disperse
vinegar	reactive
stock	bleach
dyebath	printing
jig	resist
penetrate	discharge
perforations	roller
pad stenter	transfer
pad mangles	sublimation
pressure	polyamide
washfast	polyester

Revision exercises

(1) *Double decker*

Here is a two-in-one puzzle. First, fill in the blanks in the sentences below, and then use the words to complete the crossword.

The first dyes came from _____ and _____ sources, _____ brown from cuttlefish and greens from mosses and _____.

In 1856, the first aniline _____ were discovered, producing a _____ colour.

Some fibres can absorb dyes more easily than others. _____ does not absorb dye easily, whereas _____ does. Some fibres require a _____ to help dye penetrate the fibres. Examples of mordants include _____, _____ and _____.

(2) **What am I?**

My first letter is in *mauve* and also in *vegetable*.
My second is in *mordant* and also in *orange*.
My third is in *tin* and also in *violet*.
My fourth is in *red* and also in *shade*.
My fifth is in *nylon* but *never* in *cotton*.
My last letter is in *yellow* and also in *blue*.

(3) **What am I?**

My first letter is in *mauve* but *never* in *vegetable*.
My second is in *orange* but *never* in *red*.
My third is in *disperse* but *never* in *vat*.
My fourth is in *red* but *never* in *blue*.
My fifth is in *black* and also in *cream*.
My sixth is in *pink* and also in *brown*.
My last letter is in *print* but *never* in *orange*.

What am I?

(4) **Skill test**

Answer (a), (b), (c) or (d) to the following questions.

(1) Most natural dyes are:
  (a) Colourfast
  (b) Inexpensive
  (c) Lightfast
  (d) Expensive

(2) A mordant:
  (a) Dyes fabric
  (b) Is a printing paste
  (c) Assists a fibre to absorb a dye
  (d) Is a method of printing

(3) A method of dyeing where loose fibres are dyed before spinning is:
  (a) Vat
  (b) Jig
  (c) Yarn
  (d) Stock

(4) A method of dyeing where the fabric is rolled from one roller to another through a dye bath is:
  (a) Jig
  (b) Yarn
  (c) Pad stenter
  (d) Pressure beam

(5) A method of dyeing where yarn is wound onto bobbins, placed on perforated steel rods, and then lowered into the dye bath is:
  (a) Yarn
  (b) Pad stenter
  (c) Pressure beam
  (d) Vat

(6) A synthetic dye which has good lightfastness and washfastness, and is used for nylon, polyester and acrylics is:
  (a) Sulphur
  (b) Vat
  (c) Disperse
  (d) Reactive

(7) An inexpensive dye used mainly for cottons is:
  (a) Disperse
  (b) Reactive
  (c) Vat
  (d) Direct

(8) A method of printing where a bleach removes the colour in the printed areas is called:
(a) Discharge
(b) Dyed
(c) Resist
(d) Direct

(9) A method of printing where fabric is first printed with a mordant is:
(a) Discharge   (c) Resist
(b) Dyed   (d) Direct

(10) A new method of printing using the sublimation process is:
(a) Screen
(b) Roller
(c) Transfer
(d) Block

Further reading

Davies, F. and Hatherton, S. *Materially Yours*, Longman, London, 1977

4

Textiles and the consumer

Everyone is a consumer. A consumer is anyone who buys, hires or rents services. Goods include food, clothing, shoes, cars, bikes and hairdryers. Services are provided by people at a price and include such things as medical attention, financial services, mechanical repairs and transport.

Activity

(1) List all the products made from textiles you and other class members have used in the last two weeks.
(2) Did you use any services provided by the local council or the Government? Who pays for these services?

A very large range of goods and services is available. This gives consumers freedom of choice. To choose wisely, you need to decide which purchase is best for you. Ask yourself these questions:

- Do I need it?
- Can I afford it?
- Will it do what I want it to do?
- Is the product reliable?

By asking yourself these questions, you are less likely to waste money by *impulse buying*. Impulse buying is buying goods without taking the time to consider whether they are suitable or needed.

To reduce the risk of buying fashion goods on impulse, make a habit of checking the clothing you own at the beginning of each season. Make a list of clothes that you need and buy these only. By planning your clothing needs in this way, you are much less likely to overspend or be influenced by the salesperson's comments.

The consumer's rights and responsibilities

As a consumer you have rights and responsibilities. The consumer's *rights* are:

- To buy goods that are fit for their purpose.
- To be compensated for poor-quality goods.
- To be protected by consumer laws.
- To have a choice of goods and services.

The consumer's *responsibilities* are:

- To check goods carefully before buying them.
- To check that goods can be serviced reasonably conveniently.
- To check that an article meets its advertising promise.
- To know what he or she needs and can afford.
- To compare prices.

- To read guarantees and warranties carefully.
- Never to sign a document without reading it carefully.
- To know the agencies that exist to protect consumers.

Sometimes customers have a genuine complaint. It is wise to keep dockets and receipts in case you need to return a product. When returning a product, explain the problem clearly and politely to the manager or owner of the store. If you are not given satisfaction, get advice from a consumer protection agency.

Activity

Michael bought a pair of stretch jeans. After being washed twice, they began to lose their stretch, bagging badly around the knees. Michael had followed the care label.

When he returned to the shop and asked for a refund, the shop assistant said Michael had not cared for the jeans correctly and therefore was not entitled to a refund. Michael was angry but walked out and accepted the salesperson's refusal.

(1) How could Michael have handled this situation better?
(2) What should Michael do in such a case in the future?

Consumer protection

The consumer protection agencies help people such as Michael. Protection agencies include:

- Local Authority Trading Standards Office
- Local Authority Consumer Protection Department
- Office of Fair Trading
- Environmental Health Department
- British Standards Institution

What a person buys is influenced by many factors, including:

- money ● advertising ● shop displays ● packaging ● atmosphere in the shop ● peer groups ● other people's recommendations ● consumer attitudes.

Advertising

Advertising aims to make consumers aware of a particular product and its name. Each advertisement is carefully planned to encourage a specific group of people to buy that product. Depending on the intended market, advertisements usually fall into one of the following categories:

- *Pure information* — gives factual information about the product.
- *Appeal to emotions* — associates the product with an attractive quality or lifestyle.
- *Snob appeal* — often used to sell luxury goods.
- *Sex appeal* — the product will make you attractive to the opposite sex.
- *Need to conform* — everyone else has one, so you should have one too.
- *Follow the leader* — famous people use the product.

To sell a product, a marketing campaign is usually organised. Advertising is only one aspect of the campaign. The other aspects include the actual product, how it is displayed, how it is distributed and the price.

Activity

(1) Read the following sentences. Do you agree or disagree with the statements? Place a tick next to the statements you agree with.

Advertising:
(a) Makes exaggerated and misleading claims. _____
(b) Encourages greed. _____

(continued on p. 49)

In order to give you exceptionally clean teeth the Braun rechargeable toothbrush brushes ten times faster than your usual brush at 3,300 cleaning strokes a minute.

What a mouthful.

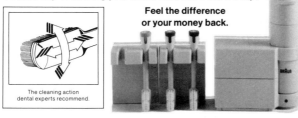

Up and down, side to side, simultaneously. Automatically. The Braun Rechargeable Toothbrush has a unique brushing action. It's the action dental experts recommend for really clean teeth and healthy gums. It's rechargeable so it maintains its brushing impetus even with all the family using it. It's simply a super-efficient way of cleaning your teeth. What more can we say?

Feel the difference or your money back.

The cleaning action dental experts recommend.

BRAUN

What type of advertising was used to sell the products in these advertisements?

CLOCK HOUSE
IMAGES CHANGE

Top.
Khaki/winter white
£14.99.
Tube skirt
Khaki or grey
£6.99.
Both in sizes 10-14

Joanne Conway
British Ladies Figure
Skating Champion.

C&A

Where value is
always in fashion

Advertising:

(c) Wastes money and increases prices. _____

(d) Encourages people to buy products they cannot afford. _____

(e) Wastes time on television and radio. _____

(f) Helps to inform consumers. _____

(g) Encourages people to work hard and save the money they need. _____

(h) Gives people new ideas. _____

Collate the responses to find the majority opinion. Have a class discussion or debate on areas where opinion is divided.

(2) Collect advertisements for textile products. Make a class display indicating how each advertisement encourages people to buy goods.

Textile performance

To meet people's needs, textile products are constantly being improved. Special finishes are given to textiles to make them suitable for particular purposes. When buying a textile product, ask these questions:

- Does it have the properties needed (e.g. crease resistant)?
- Will it need special laundering?
- How durable is it?

The following tests are not scientific. They allow you to test the following properties of fibres without the need for complicated equipment:

- Appearance — crease and wrinkle resistance
- Durability — abrasion resistance
- Comfort — thermal properties, absorbency.

What features of clothing would be important in motor racing?

Flammability

Most textile fabrics will burn, except for asbestos, which is considered *fireproof*. Terms used to indicate the amount textiles will burn include *flame retardant* and *flame resistant*. These terms mean that the flammability is reduced, so the fabric will burn slowly.

It has been found that many accidents in the home are caused by textiles catching alight. To safeguard consumers, legislation sets standards for such things as nightwear, mattresses, carpets and rugs.

The finish applied to a fabric must also be considered, for it may increase the fabric's flammability.

Activity

(1) Look carefully at the nightwear shown below (left). List the features of the style.
(2) Design a style yourself with safety features.

Know your safer nightwear labels

These are some of the labels that appear on children's nightwear:

Low flammability to BS 5722 — Fabric has passed the test for low flammability required for night-dresses, pyjamas and dressing gowns.

Flame retardant — Made of fabric with low flammability.

WARNING — KEEP AWAY FROM FIRE — Made from fabric which is not considered to be of low flammability.

Activity

You will need

- 6 fabric samples 6 cm × 35 cm — wool, cotton, nylon, acetate, flannelette and rayon
- 6 bulldog clips
- 2 retort stands
- Metal drip tray
- Matches

Method

Ribbing

Ribbing

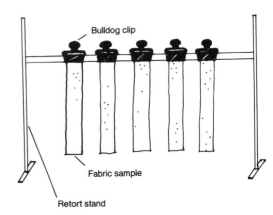

Bulldog clip

Fabric sample

Retort stand

(1) Attach the fabric to stands with bulldog clips, as shown in the diagram.
(2) Place drip tray underneath to protect furniture.
(3) Place a lighted match at the lower end of the first sample.
(4) Observe and record the result. Repeat for each sample.

Results

Which fabric:

    (a) Burnt?
    (b) Melted?
    (c) Was self extinguishing?

(The flammability of fabrics may be temporarily reduced by applying a mixture of Borax and boric acid solution.)

(2) Which fabric would you make pyjamas from? Give your reasons.

Resistance to abrasion

Fabrics differ in their ability to withstand abrasion (or rubbing). The effect of abrasion is evident on corduroy jeans when the pile fabric is worn, leaving shiny 'bald' areas.

Activity

You will need

- 2 wooden blocks
- Very fine sandpaper
- Drawing pins
- Fabric samples

Method

(1) Pin a fabric sample to one wooden block and sandpaper to the other block.
(2) Rub sandpaper over the fabric. Record the results. Repeat with the other samples.

Note: This test will wear fabric more quickly than normal wear. Comparisons will be accurate if all the fabric samples are rubbed with sandpaper for the same time and with the same pressure.

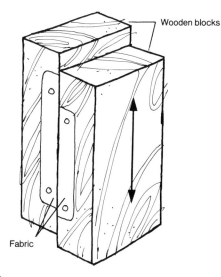

Wooden blocks

Fabric

Results

Which fabric was:
(a) Least affected?
(b) Quickly worn?
(c) Not changed?

Fabrics as insulators

We wear clothes to keep us warm or cool. Some fabrics are more suitable than others for these purposes.

Activity

You will need

- 5 tins (all the same size)
- 5 thermometers
- 10 elastic bands
- 5 samples of different fabrics

Method

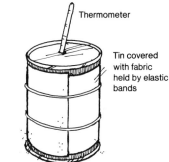

Thermometer

Tin covered with fabric held by elastic bands

(1) Cut fabric to fit around the outside of the tin. Secure with elastic bands.
(2) Place a thermometer in the centre of each tin.
(3) Record the temperature after 15 minutes.

Results

Which fabric is:
(a) Warm? (b) Cool?

Crease resistance

Some fabrics are naturally crease resistant but others need to have special finishes so they will recover quickly from wrinkling. Garments such as trousers and pleated skirts need a sharp crease or pleat which will stay in permanently. Such garments can be specially treated and labelled 'permanent press'. They wrinkle very little during wear and can be washed very easily. The creases or pleats will not come out and they should not need ironing.

Activity

You will need

- Samples of different fabrics 10 cm × 10 cm
- A watch or clock to time seconds.

Method

(1) Crumple each sample of fabric in your hand and hold it tightly for 10 seconds.
(2) Open your hand and lay the fabric on the table. Notice how quickly the different fabrics recover from the creasing.

Results

Which fabric recovered from creasing:
(a) most quickly; (b) least quickly?

Shrinkage

During weaving fibres stretch. If they are wetted they go back to their original size and the fabric shrinks. Natural fibres absorb moisture easily and as the fibre swells widthways, it shrinks along its length. Different methods are used to pre-shrink fabrics and it may be combined with a crease resistant finish. Cheap cotton, some wool, rayon and curtain fabrics are the most likely to shrink.

Activity

You will need

- Samples of different fabric cut on the grain exactly 20 cm × 20 cm
- An iron and a damp pressing cloth.

Method

(1) Mark the warp grain of the fabric.
(2) Cover the sample with the damp pressing cloth.
(3) Press with a hot iron until dry.
(4) Measure the length and width.

Results

Calculate the percentage of shrinkage.

$$\text{Shrinkage} = \frac{\text{Original size} - \text{Final size}}{\text{Original size}} \times 100$$

Why is shrinkage calculated separately for the length and width?

Labels

The development of a labelling system for textiles has been a benefit to consumers. Labels give information about the care a particular garment needs and any special properties or finishes the fabric offers. A small label sewn into the garment is the most suitable form of labelling.

A good label will give the following information:

- Fibre content
- Special finish or treatments
- Cleaning instructions
- Size of garment.

The following symbols are used on labels. They explain how to care for a product.

Washing

Article can be washed.

Maximum water temperature to be used.

Do not wash.

Bleaching

Article can be bleached.

Hypochlorite *or* chlorine bleach can be used.

Do not bleach with hypochlorite bleach.

Do not bleach.

Drying

Article can be tumble dried.

Dry flat.

Drip dry soaking wet.

Hang to dry.

Ironing

Article can be ironed.

Use a cool iron.

Use a hot iron.

Use a warm iron.

Do not iron.

Drycleaning

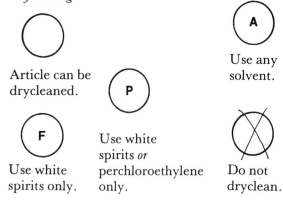

Article can be drycleaned.

Use white spirits only.

Use white spirits *or* perchloroethylene only.

Use any solvent.

Do not dryclean.

Activity

(1) Each student is to bring to class two labels. Divide the labels into two groups:

    (a) Those with all the information a consumer needs to know.

    (b) Those that need more information. List the information missing in each case.

(2) Design labels for:

    (a) A fleecy-lined cotton/polyester windcheater.

    (b) A pure wool blazer.

Textiles and the environment

The production of textiles involves certain hazards and costs to consumers.

Textile workers may suffer lung diseases as a result of handling asbestos and glass fibres. The noise of some equipment can cause hearing loss.

Pollution of water and air from textile processing has upset the *ecology* in some areas. Fines are now imposed on people who dump waste in streams and rivers. Nowadays detergent is used more often than soap for home laundering. Detergent does not break down as quickly as soap. It is said to be not as *biodegradable*.

Another resource to be considered is energy. Drying clothes naturally and greater use of drip-dry fabrics will reduce the amount of electricity used for irons and clothes dryers.

Be a wise consumer. By choosing textile products carefully, you will save your own time and money and also the limited natural resources available to us all.

Pollution at its worst. How can we avoid pollution in the textile industry?

Words to remember

consumer	flammability
impulse	properties
retardant	pollution
fireproof	ecology
resistant	asbestos

Revision exercises

(1) Explain the difference between goods and services.
(2) What are the disadvantages of impulse buying?
(3) List the advantages of advertising.
(4) Explain the difference between fireproof and flame retardant.
(5) What are the advantages of labels to consumers?
(6) Discuss the effect textile production has on the environment.

Extension activity 1

Find these words in the wonderword, and then use the left-over letters to make a sentence.

consumer	Borax
textile	noise
services	silk
clothing	peer
impulse	abrasion
buying	ban
apparel	durable
rights	shrinkage
responsibilities	comfort
symbols	appearance
care	environment
nylon	pollution
use	standard
standard	energy
finance	labels
protection	clean
inform	store
emotions	stain
market	rayon
flame	safe
nightwear	

Using the left-over letters, complete the sentence:

`__ __ _ ____ _____ ____ ____`
`_____ _____ _____.`

```
C O N S U M E R I G H T S Y M B O L S
L T O E M O T I O N S H R I N K A G E
O E P R E S P O N S I B I L I T I E S
T N O V B E D N I G H T W E A R D P D
H V L I M P U L S E S A F E L R M R A
I I L C W I R C O M F O R T A A A O S
N R U E E C A O T L C I N D R D B T S
G O T S E R B P A E N L N K N U A E M
N N I E E N L M P F A A E A L I N C L
I M O S E R E E O A T T A N I U T R
Y E N R A R E R R S R S I O N C S I A
U N O E A R M O G D C E I L A R E O Y
B T E L A B B E L Y S S L F E I R N O
S A P P E A R A N C E S T N Y L O N N
```

Extension activity 2

Group decision making (1)

The class is to become a clothing company. Hold a company meeting to carry out the following tasks. (Divide into two or more groups if necessary.)

(1) Determine the most useful talents of each member. This will help the class decide what position each person should have in the company.
(2) Decide on the product the company will make.
(3) Survey the school population to determine if there is a market for your product.
(4) Make advertising posters for the product.
(5) Design a label for your product.
(6) Consider your company's image. What type of people do you particularly want to attract as consumers of your product?

Group decision making (2)

(1) Plan a fashion magazine for your school.
(2) Using a scrapbook, make a pilot copy that can be shown to prospective consumers in your school.
(3) After considering the comments of future consumers, consider any changes that can be made to improve the likely circulation.

Extension activity 3

(1) List, step by step, what should be done if a small child's nightwear caught alight.

(2) How would you treat an injury caused by burning clothes?
(3) Suppose a child is wearing a *synthetic* nightgown, which catches alight.
   (a) What would happen to the synthetic fabric?
   (b) How should this burn be treated? Explain.

Glossary

Fireproof — Will not burn in flame.
Flammability — The readiness with which something burns. In the case of fabrics, this is determined by the fibre content and the fabric weight.
Ecology — The study of how animals interact with their environment.
Retardant — A retardant slows down the onset of fire.

Further reading

Bird, J. and Catherall, E. *Fibres and Fabrics,* McDonald Educational, London, 1977
Ridley, A. and Williams, D. *Simple Experiments in Textile Science,* Heinemann Educational, London, 1974

5

Textile yarns

A yarn is a long strand of fibres twisted together so that it is strong enough to use for making fabric or sewing fabrics together.

Yarns can be made from staple fibres such as wool, cotton and linen. In fact all natural fibres occur in the staple form except silk.

Silk and man-made fibres are all filament fibres. These can be made into monofilament, multifilament or staple spun yarns.

A *monofilament* yarn has only one filament, which is often fine, as used for pantyhose and socks.

A *multifilament* yarn contains many filaments. It usually stretches more easily than monofilament yarns and is more useful, being made into fabrics, ropes and various fibre-blend yarns.

Staple spun yarns are bulky yarns made from staple fibres. They are usually soft, fuzzy and used for warm fabrics such as brushed flannelette and woollen knits.

Activity

Paste a sample of a monofilament, multi-filament and staple yarn into your workbook.

Spinning methods

The simplest method of spinning by hand is to twist fibres, using either a spindle or spinning wheel. In many parts of the world these methods of spinning, which were invented in ancient times, are still used today. In countries

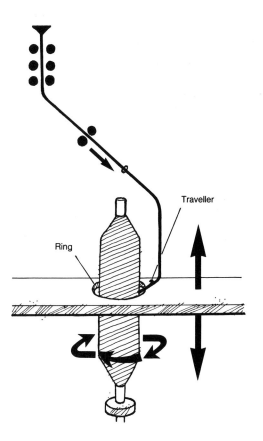

Ring spinning

such as India, Argentina and Chile, hand spinning is the main method of producing yarn. Even though hand spinning is a slow process, interesting yarns can be produced that would be difficult to produce by machine.

Wheel and spindle spinning are relaxing leisure crafts for many people in Britain Pleasure can be gained by producing your own garment from the raw fibres through to the finished product. Each design is unique, because no two people will spin yarn exactly the same.

The first type of electrically powered spinning machine was called a spinning jenny. Invented by James Hargreaves in Britain in 1765, it made cloth making a more sophisticated process. The spinning jenny allowed many threads to be spun at the same time.

In industrialised societies today, the most common type of spinning method is *ring spinning* (see figure on p. 57).

The ring around the bobbin guides the traveller, which revolves around the bobbin several thousand times per minute. A spinning frame may consist of hundreds of bobbins.

Open-end spinning is a new method, which produces yarn faster than ring spinning and so saves costs. Fibres attach themselves to a 'seed yarn' after being passed through compressed air. The motor rotates at 20 000 to 40 000 revolutions per minute.

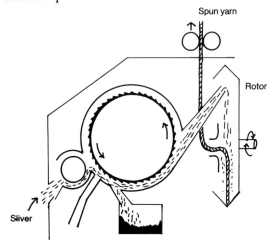

Open-end spinning

Twist

Yarns can be twisted to the right or to the left. If yarns are twisted to the right, they form an *S twist*. If they are twisted to the left, they form a *Z twist*.

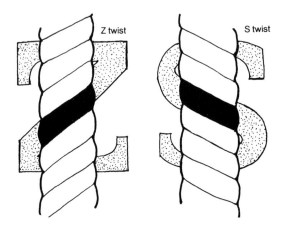

Direction of yarn twist

The number of times a yarn is twisted affects its properties. For example, some yarns can be twisted tightly, and this produces a coarse fabric.

The direction of the twist determines the plying behaviour of the yarn. Plying is the process of twisting two or more yarns together; for example, four monofilament yarns might be twisted together to form one multifilament yarn. The monofilament yarns would be S twisted to form a Z twisted multifilament.

Activity

Take a thick plyed yarn and untwist it. In which direction are the individual yarns twisted?

Textured yarns

Straight yarns may be crimped or bulked to alter their appearance and properties. Thermoplastic yarns, such as the synthetics nylon, Orlon and Terylene, lend themselves to texturing, as they can be heat set into different shapes.

A stuffer box is used to produce textured yarns. The multifilament yarn is overfed into a heated box. The softened yarn folds (or crimps) and sets in the crimped shape as it cools to room temperature on leaving the stuffer box. Crimping gives yarns such as Orlon the soft, fluffy appearance of wool.

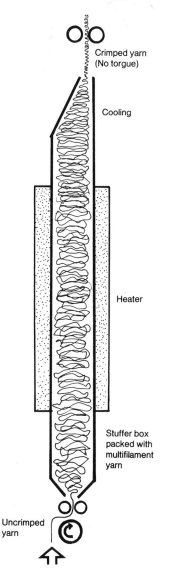

Crimped yarn (No torgue)

Cooling

Heater

Stuffer box packed with multifilament yarn

Uncrimped yarn

Crimping yarn in a stuffer box

False twist texturing is another way of making soft, bulky yarns from straight ones. Again, thermoplastic synthetic yarns must be used, because they can be heat set while being twisted. The machine swings the twist from S to Z as the yarn is being spun. As the yarn is heat set as it is spun, the twist does not unwind.

Yarn twisted in S direction   Yarn twisted in Z direction

Activity

Try to false twist a length of synthetic yarn such as nylon or Terylene. Heat set the yarn into place with an iron, and then twist the yarn in the opposite direction and reset it. *Remember:* use a hot iron and place a cotton cloth between the synthetic yarn and the iron, or the synthetic yarn will stick to the iron.

Novelty yarns

Combinations of different yarn types, twists and textures produce interesting *novelty* yarns. The following are the most common types of novelty yarns:

- *Loop yarns* — Two yarns with circular loops at even intervals.

Loop

- *Bouclé yarn* — One yarn with tight loops at varying intervals.

Soft bouclé overtwisted yarn   Leader yarn

- *Slub yarn* — A thick, lightly twisted yarn (slub) with a thin tie yarn twisted tightly around it. A slub yarn has an uneven appearance.

Slub of roving   Tie yarn

- *Knop or knot yarn* — Two yarns, with an enlarged thickness at irregular intervals produced by one yarn being twisted back over itself.

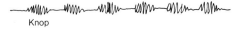
Knop

- *Worsted yarn* — A smooth, highly twisted yarn made from a long staple. The fibres are combed to make them lie parallel to each other before spinning. Used to make fine suiting fabrics.

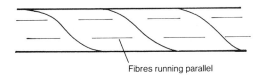
Fibres running parallel

- *Laminated metallic yarns* — A narrow strip of aluminium forms the centre part of the yarn. As aluminium doesn't twist easily, finer yarns of cotton or polyester are twisted around it.

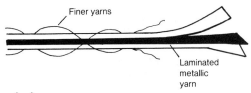
Finer yarns
Laminated metallic yarn

Activity

Collect some novelty yarns and try to identify them. Paste them in your workbook, and label them.

Blending fibres to make yarns

Various types of fibres can be blended. Some common ones are polyester and cotton, polyester and wool, and nylon and wool. By blending fibres, the advantages of each fibre are combined in the one yarn. For example, polyester does not require ironing and cotton absorbs moisture, so a cotton-polyester blend yarn is often used for shirts, making them easy to wash and comfortable to wear.

Yarns are blended by playing them in the opposite direction to their original twist.

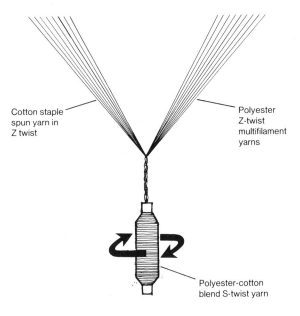
Cotton staple spun yarn in Z twist
Polyester Z-twist multifilament yarns
Polyester-cotton blend S-twist yarn

Words to remember

twist	worsted
monofilament yarn	combing
multifilament yarn	carding
staple yarn	bouclé
roving	thermoplastic
spindle	heat-set yarns
ring spinning	texturing
open-end spinning	crimping
sliver	knop
bulked yarns	blending
slub	loop

Revision exercise 1

Yarns skill test

Answer (a), (b), (c) or (d) to the following questions.

(1) The rotating device used in spinning is a:
(a) Roving
(b) Bulking machine
(c) Spindle
(d) Drafter

(2) The only natural fibre that is a filament fibre is:
(a) Silk
(b) Wool
(c) Jute
(d) Flax

(3) A new method of spinning yarn where the fibres attach to a seed yarn is:
(a) Ring spinning
(b) Open-end spinning
(c) Wheel spinning
(d) Spindle spinning

(4) A novelty yarn that includes laminated aluminium is:
(a) Bouclé
(b) Loop
(c) Metallic
(d) Knop

(5) A novelty yarn that has uneven loops at intervals along it is:
(a) Worsted
(b) Loop
(c) Knop
(d) Bouclé

(6) A smooth, fine yarn used for suiting fabrics is:
(a) Worsted
(b) Woollen
(c) Knop
(d) Metallic

(7) A yarn that has a thick, uneven roving as its base is:
(a) Loop
(b) Knop
(c) Woollen
(d) Slub

(8) Twisting two or more yarns together is called:
(a) Crimping
(b) Plying
(c) Blending
(d) Texturing

(9) A yarn that cannot be crimped in a stuffer box is:
(a) Wool
(b) Terylene
(c) Nylon
(d) Orlon

(10) A method of spinning that produces a bulky, soft yarn is:
(a) False twist texturing
(b) Knopping
(c) Blending
(d) Open-end spinning

Revision exercise 2

Odd one out

Can you pick the word that is out of place in each group?

(1) Silk, wool, nylon, flax, jute
(2) Open-end spinning, ring spinning, spinning jenny, drop spinning
(3) Loop, slub, bouclé, roving
(4) Nylon, cotton, heat set, thermoplastic
(5) Silk, nylon, Orlon, wool, polyester
(6) Z twist, K twist, S twist
(7) False twist, texturising, bulking, crimping, blending
(8) Worsted, woollen, drawing, slub

Revision exercise 3

Using the clues, fill in the missing words:

M------------ (13)
O-------------- (4/3/8)
N------ (7)
O---- (5)
F----- (6)
-I-- (4)
L--- (4)
--A---- (4/3)
M------- (8)
--E---------- (13)
N---- (5)
T---- (5)

Clues

M A yarn containing many filaments
O Spinning method where fibres attach them-
  selves to a 'seed yarn'
N These fibres usually produce staple yarn
O A yarn that is bulked to resemble wool
F Are spun to make yarn
I A natural monofilament fibre
L A type of novelty yarn
A A process used in producing textured yarns
M A yarn with a base of laminated aluminium
E The property of synthetic yarns that allows
  them to be heat set
N A thermoplastic yarn
T S and Z indicate its direction

6

Constructing fabric

There are many ways of constructing (or putting together) fabric. Fabrics may be woven, knitted, felted, bonded, crocheted, knotted (as in macrame) or braided. Most of these methods involve interlacing yarns in some way.

Knitting

Hand knitting has a long history. The first knitting needles were made from bones, but today they are usually plastic or aluminium.

However, most knitted fabrics are now produced by machine.

The simplest form of knitting, which is used to make fabrics for such things as T-shirts, swimsuits and jumpers, is *weft* knitting. In weft knitting, the yarn forms horizontal rows of loops across the fabric. *Single jersey* is made on a machine which has one set of needles. If a plain stitch is used it resembles hand knitted stocking stitch.

In weft knitting a horizontal row of loops in the fabric is known as a *course* and a vertical row of loops as a *wale*. Notice in the diagram how the yarn is looped horizontally and vertically, forming courses and wales.

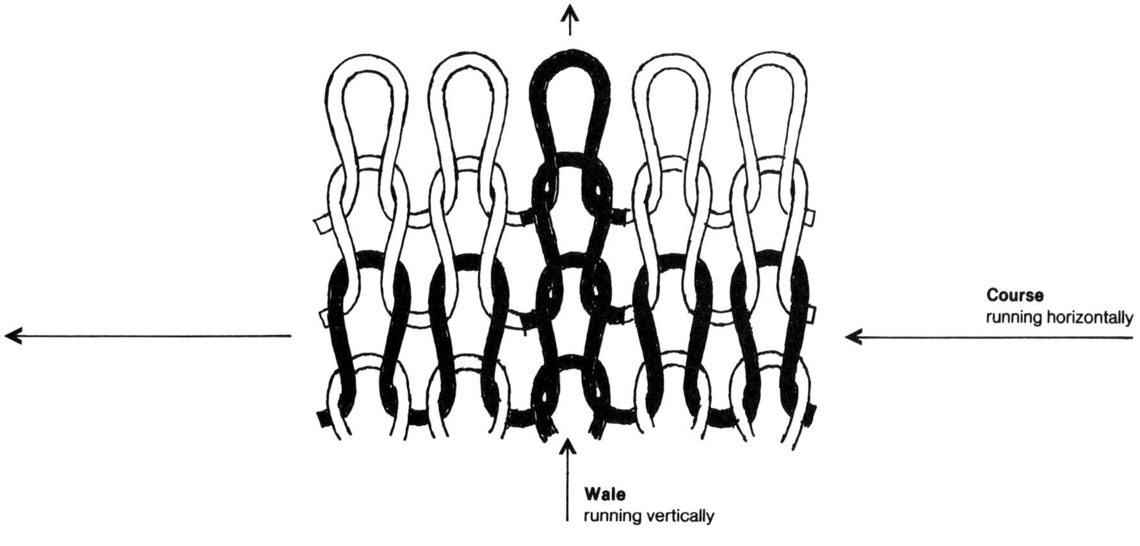

Course
running horizontally

Wale
running vertically

Many rows of latch hooks are used in the manufacture of knitted fabric. There is one latch hook for each wale in the fabric. The diagram shows how loops are formed with latch hooks.

A latch hook

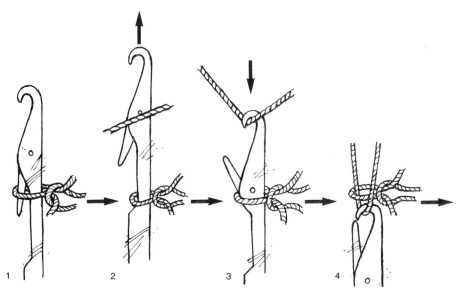

Activity

Using either a crochet hook, a rug hook or your forefinger, loop a length of yarn to form a single wale. Paste this in your workbook.

Knitted fabrics can be made with either a circular or flat machine. Fabrics for stockings, socks and T-shirts are knitted on a circular machine like the one in the photograph.

Fabrics knitted on a circular machine are tubular. The straight grain of the fabric is indicated by the wale, as there is no *selvedge* as on woven fabrics. Flat knitting machines, where the yarn travels across the needle bed rather than moving around, are used to make garments such as jumpers.

Activity

Collect as many different knit constructions as you can. Try to classify them as one of the types listed in the following sections.

Weft knits

Single jersey

This is a simple form of weft knitting using one yarn, which travels across the fabric. Used for garments such as T-shirts and windcheaters.

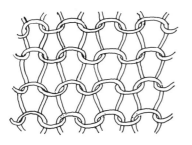

Double jersey

Two rows of weft knitting are interlocked, back and front, so that they cannot be separated. They have a stocking stitch appearance on both sides. This gives the fabric built-in stability, making it suitable for tailored garments such as slacks, coats and waistcoats.

Rib jersey

Purl and plain interlocking are combined in the same row, producing a very elastic jersey. Used for cuffs on jumpers and windcheaters, and socks.

Warp knits

Tricot

Many yarns are used to form this type of knit. Each needle has its own yarn and is knitted vertically. Tricot drapes well and is usually very soft and elastic. It is also run resistant. (If you are unsure whether a fabric sample is a warp knit, see if one of the wales drops a loop or 'runs'. If it does not, then it is probably a warp knit.) Tricot is very useful for underwear and stockings.

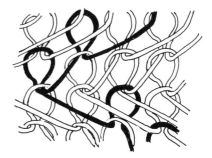

Raschel

This is a very open, lacy warp knit, used for fashion wear and as a backing for bonded fabrics, where two fabrics are glued together to give greater strength and stability.

Weaving

In the weaving process, two sets of threads are interlaced at right angles to each other. The threads that run parallel to or at the same angle as the selvedge are called the *warp* threads. The *weft* or *filling* threads run at right angles to the selvedge and are usually not as strong as the warp threads.

The warp threads are set up first on the *weaving loom*. Weaving looms range from simple constructions in the form of a wooden rectangular frame or a circular ring to the large automatic looms used in the manufacturing process called Sulzer looms.

There are many ways in which the weft yarn can be interlaced with the warp yarns when weaving. These different patterns produce fabrics with varying colours and handling properties. The simplest of all weaves is the *plain weave*.

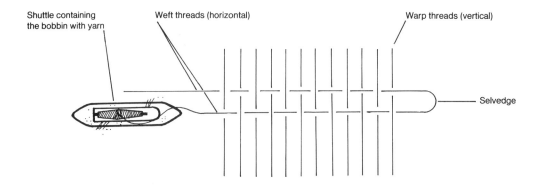

The weaving process: the weft threads are interlaced through the warp.

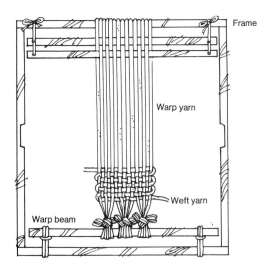

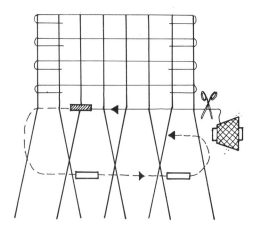

Simple frame loom set up for plain weaving   Sulzer Loom operation

Activity — Plain weaving

(1) Take two different-coloured 7.5 cm squares, and cut one square into 6 mm strips. These strips are to be used as the weft threads. Cut the other square into 6 mm strips after folding it in half, leaving a 6 mm edge as shown.

(2) Using the weft threads, weave one thread under and then over the next warp thread. Repeat this along the line. In the next row, weave the weft thread over and then under the next warp thread. Repeat this pattern until all the weft threads are used. You should end with a sample like this:

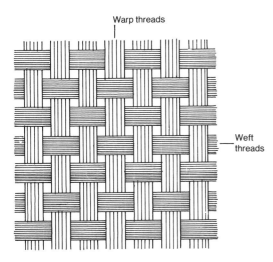

Warp threads

Weft threads

(3) Paste this sample in your workbook, together with a piece of plain weave fabric such as cotton calico, organdie or lawn.

Textile designers draw weave patterns on graph paper. Each square represents the crossing of yarns. If a square is blank, the weft yarn passes *over* the warp. If a square is filled in, the weft yarn passes *under* the warp.

The weave pattern for plain weave looks like this:

A variation of plain weave is *basket weave*. The weave pattern for basket weave looks like this:

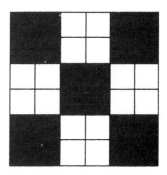

Basket weave fabrics include sailcloth and hopsack. These fabrics resist tearing, because there are two pairs of yarns in each direction.

Activity

Using coloured squares, make samples for your workbook using any of the following weave types.

Twill weave

Twill weave produces diagonal lines on the cloth. The weft thread moves one warp yarn to the left or right on each new row. This method usually produces a strong fabric, such as gabardine, denim and wool serge.

Herringbone twill weave

Reversing the direction from time to time in a twill weave makes patterns like bones in a herring fish. This weave gives a very distinct decorative effect.

Satin weave

In this type of weaving, long floating warp threads are produced by passing weft threads at irregular intervals under four or more warp threads. These long strands, called *floats*, give satin, rayon and silk woven in this way their shiny appearance. The longer the floats, the more likely the fabric is to catch on rough surfaces.

Jacquard weave

Invented by a Frenchman called Jacquard, this weave forms intricate designs. Patterns are punched onto computer cards which are placed into the machine to direct the raising of the warp threads. Each row is different from the previous one. Such patterns produce intricate designs for towels or damask tablecloths. Where two colours are used in the weft, the back of the fabric gives a reverse colour to the front.

Activity

Find a sample of a Jacquard weave fabric for your workbook. No one could draw a pattern for this!

Gauze or Leno weave

The warp yarns are twisted in pairs during the weaving process, forming a very strong fabric.

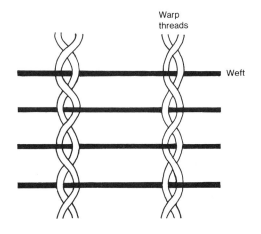

Curtain fabrics are often made with this weave.

Pile weave

An extra set of warp or weft yarns is used to produce a raised surface on plain or twill weave fabric. Pile weave is used for towelling, corduroy, velvet and carpet. For towelling, loops can be made on one or both sides of the fabric.

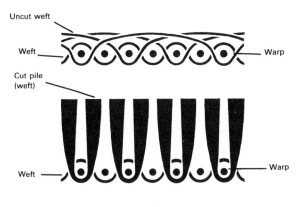

A cross-section through a pile weave

Activity

Find a sample of a cut and uncut pile weave fabric for your workbook.

Using a pick glass

Sometimes it is difficult to identify a weave pattern without a magnifying glass. A *pick glass* is a measuring and magnifying instrument. Weft threads are sometimes called *picks*, and the pick glass is used to count the number of weft threads per centimetre woven in a fabric.

The warp and weft yarns in woven fabrics may be closely or tightly packed. Loose weaving produces a cloth that drapes well but may not be very durable. Tighter weaves have more yarns per centimetre and produce strong, less flexible fabric.

Activity

(1) Using a pick glass, identify the warp and weft threads in a number of different fabric samples. The warp is usually easy to identify if there is a selvedge, as the warp runs parallel to the selvedge. If there is no selvedge, stretch the fabric in both directions — the weft usually extends further than the warp.

(2) Now draw a 1 cm square on your fabric sample, and, using the pick glass, count the number of warp and weft yarns.

Results

Record your results in your workbook in a table like the following:

Fabric sample	Weft yarns/cm	Warp yarns/cm

Conclusion

(1) Are the yarns spaced more closely in the warp or the weft direction? Why?
(2) How does the number of warp and weft yarns per centimetre affect the use to which a fabric is put?

Activities

(1) *Creative weaving*

Circular or cardboard looms can be used to create interesting weavings.

To make a circular loom, bend a piece of cane into a circle, and then wrap the warp around it. Use various textured yarns and combed fibres such as wool to weave segments. Always draw and label a plan of the finished design before you start. The diagram acts as a pattern to follow.

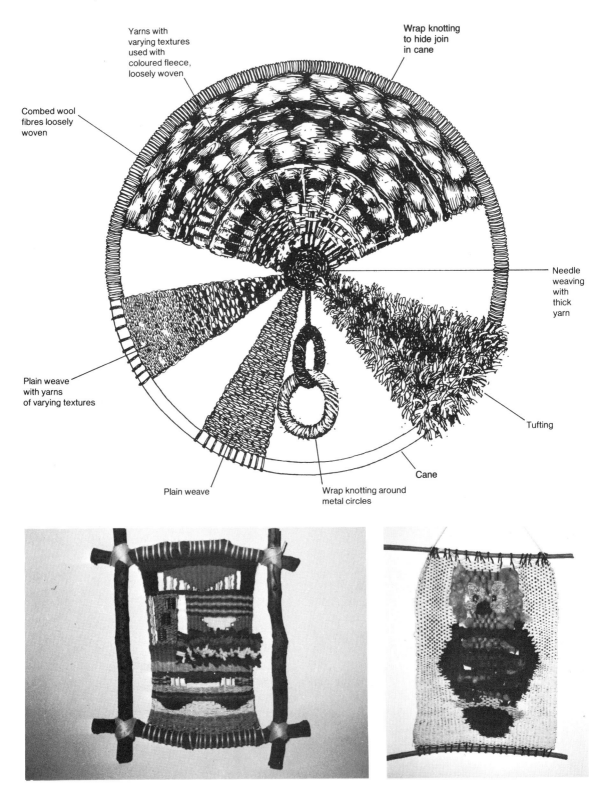

Yarns with varying textures used with coloured fleece, loosely woven

Wrap knotting to hide join in cane

Combed wool fibres loosely woven

Needle weaving with thick yarn

Plain weave with yarns of varying textures

Tufting

Cane

Plain weave

Wrap knotting around metal circles

(2) *Inkle loom weaving*

The inkle loom dates back to the first century A.D. The word 'inkle' refers to narrow woven bands or tapes.

The equipment is simple and inexpensive. You need a sturdy frame to hold the *warp* (lengthwise) yarns under tension and a shuttle to carry the weft yarns through the warp. The shuttle can be made from a ruler or a thin piece of wood.

A variety of yarns can be used for inkle weaving. Cotton and linen are the best, as they are smooth and strong. Avoid yarns that stretch under tension.

The *heddles* for inkle loom weaving are made from string and are placed on every second warp thread to produce a space (the *shed*) for plain weaving.

The *dowel rods* on the inkle loom act as a guide for the warp threads as they are placed on the loom.

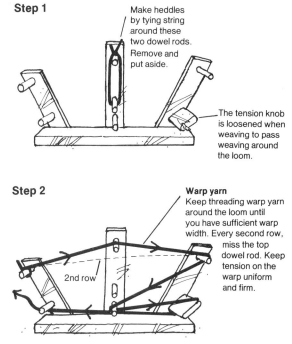

Step 1

Make heddles by tying string around these two dowel rods. Remove and put aside.

The tension knob is loosened when weaving to pass weaving around the loom.

Step 2

Warp yarn
Keep threading warp yarn around the loom until you have sufficient warp width. Every second row, miss the top dowel rod. Keep tension on the warp uniform and firm.

2nd row

An Inkle loom set up for weaving a belt or tie

Step 3

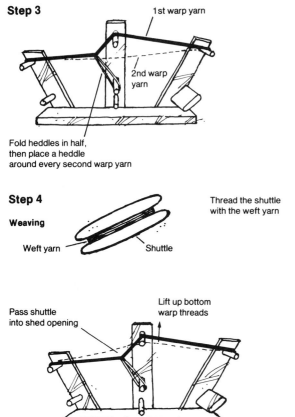

1st warp yarn

2nd warp yarn

Fold heddles in half, then place a heddle around every second warp yarn

Step 4

Weaving

Weft yarn — Shuttle

Thread the shuttle with the weft yarn

The *tension knob* is tightened when the warp threads are placed on the loom and then loosened during weaving to allow the shed to be created without undue stress on the warp threads.

Patterns are created either by using a number of different-coloured weft yarns on separate shuttles or by lifting different warp yarns at different times.

A plain weave is produced by lifting every second warp thread and then reversing the warp threads in the next row. Variations can be made by lifting different warp threads. Try making designs by using various colours for the warp and weft yarns as well as by varying the pattern of warp threads lifted.

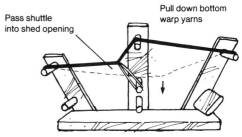

Pass shuttle into shed opening

Lift up bottom warp threads

Pass shuttle into shed opening

Pull down bottom warp yarns

To finish weaving
Cut the warp yarns and finish by tying or sewing the ends

---

(3) *Eight-shaft loom weaving*

With this type of loom, the eight levers can be used to create different patterns.

By lowering levers the *shafts* are raised thus creating a *shed*. This is the space between the two layers of warp through which the shuttle is passed. Interesting patterns are produced and the use of different colours and textures gives further variations.

Set up the loom by passing warp yarns through each of the heddles. Tie securely on one end, and wind up the length on the *cloth beam*. The cloth beam is a roller on the side of the loom that winds around to take up the fabric as it is woven. Number the eight shafts on the top of the lever right to left from 1 to 8.

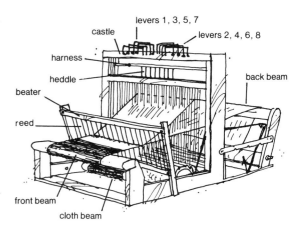

castle
levers 1, 3, 5, 7
levers 2, 4, 6, 8
harness
heddle
back beam
beater
reed
front beam
cloth beam

The eight-shaft loom

Experiment with the levers to create different patterns. Here are some for you to try. (Do 10 rows of plain weave first.)

Row 1: 1, 3, 5, 7
Row 2: 2, 4, 6, 8
Repeat rows 1, 2

Pattern 1

Row 1: Bring up levers 2, 3, 6, 7
Row 2: Bring up levers 1, 3, 5, 7
Row 3: Bring up levers 3, 4, 7, 8
Row 4: Bring up levers 1, 3, 5, 7
Row 5: Bring up levers 1, 4, 5, 8
Row 6: Bring up levers 1, 3, 5, 7
Row 7: Bring up levers 1, 2, 5, 6
Row 8: Bring up levers 1, 3, 5, 7
Row 9: Bring up levers 2, 3, 6, 7
Row 10: Bring up levers 1, 3, 5, 7
Row 11: Bring up levers 1, 2, 5, 6
Row 12: Bring up levers 1, 3, 5, 7
Row 13: Bring up levers 1, 4, 5, 8
Row 14: Bring up levers 1, 3, 5, 7
Row 15: Bring up levers 3, 4, 7, 8
Row 16: Bring up levers 1, 3, 5, 7

Do 6 rows of plain weave before the next pattern.

Pattern 2

Row 1: Bring up levers 1, 3, 5, 7 dark weft yarn
Row 2: Bring up levers 2, 4, 6, 8 dark weft yarn
Row 3: Bring up levers 1, 3, 5, 7 light weft yarn
Row 4: Bring up levers 2, 4, 6, 8 dark weft yarn
Row 5: Bring up levers 1, 3, 5, 7 dark weft yarn
Row 6: Bring up levers 2, 4, 6, 8 light weft yarn

Pattern 3

Use the same plain weave pattern (1, 3, 5, 7) then (2, 4, 6, 8) and weave:

2 rows dark yarn
1 row light yarn
1 row dark yarn
1 row light yarn
1 row dark yarn
4 rows light yarn

Remember: Always leave a plain weave border of 6 to 10 rows between your weaving experiments, and record your pattern of levers as you go.

A shoulder bag woven from wool yarn

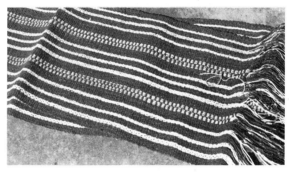

Yarn made from bark was used to weave this cloth.

Non-woven fabrics

Not all fabrics are made by interlacing yarns. Some are made directly from the fibres. *Felt*, for example, is made from wool fibres by a process involving heat, moisture and pressure.

Felt can also be made from rayon, fur or cotton fibres or combinations of these with wool.

As the fibres are not securely fastened, felted fabrics are not very strong and pull apart easily. This means that they cannot be washed, but they can be sponged clean with warm soapy water. Felt does not fray or unravel, so it is ideal for hats, slippers, fancy dress costumes and as backing for wooden or metal ornaments to prevent scratching and slipping.

In *bonding*, fibres are laid out in sheets and an adhesive glue is applied under heat and pressure. This is a cheap method of producing interfacing fabrics for stiffening clothing and such things as disposable dishcloths.

Non-woven paddings and underlays can be produced by *needling*. Barbed needles are pushed into fibre webs to interlock and tangle the fibres as they move up and down. Such materials are used for disposable nappies and towels.

Tufting is the most common method of making pile floor coverings. The tufting machine has several hundred needles, which extend across the width of a broadloom carpet. As the needles push down, the backing fabric moves a short distance to create the loop. The back is then sealed with latex rubber to prevent the loops from being pulled out.

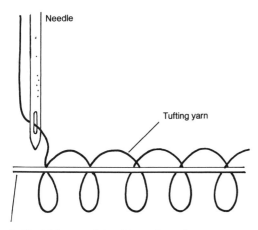

Needle

Tufting yarn

Backing fabric — usually hessian or polypropylene

A cross section of the tufting process

Activities

(1) Try making your own non-woven fabric. Soak some wool fibres in *hot* water and then iron between two pieces of paper using heavy pressure. You should now have a piece of felt. What effect does the heat have on the wool fibres to cause them to felt?

(2) Collect samples of non-woven fabric for your workbook. Label them as either felted, bonded, tufted or needle punched.

Words to remember

warp	plain weave
weft	basket weave
loom	satin weave
shuttle	Jacquard weave
bonding	Leno or gauze weave
felting	twill weave
fibre web	herringbone weave
heddle	pile weave
bobbins	gabardine
pick glass	hopsack
Sulzer loom	terry towelling
double jersey	damask
tricot	calico
raschel	organdie
selvedge	sailcloth
parallel	draping
wale	mesh
course	eight-shaft loom
latch needle	inkle loom
felt	tufting
shed	

Revision exercises

(1) *Double confusion*

The following groups of letters each contain two words that are related in some way. Use the clues to help you unscramble the words.

e.g. (1) Horizontal and vertical interlacing in the construction of knitted fabric
LWEAOECRUS

Answer wale/course

(2) The two most common methods of constructing cloth
NTGKINTEVGIWNA

(3) An instrument used to make fabric
A LHCTATENDEEEL

(4) Two types of knit fabric construction, also used in weaving terminology
APWRWTEF

(5) Two types of warp knits
CTTIROSLERCAH

(6) Two methods of making carpets
FUTTGNIILEEWVPAE

(7) Bonding fibres is usually done under
TEHAEPSSRURE

(8) A weaving process in which the warp yarns are twisted
OLNEAZGUE

(9) Parts of a weaving loom
EDLDHEUTSTHEL

(10) Common, similar weaves
ESBKATILNPA

(2) *Complete the pattern*

Complete the missing row in the following weave patterns, first copying them on graph paper. Paste them in your workbook, labelling each weave type.

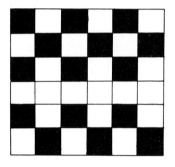

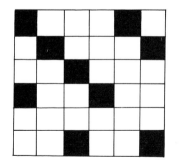

76

7

Design

In medieval times, tailors were known as *cissorii*. They cut out and made up both men's and women's clothing. It is not surprising, then, that men's and women's fashions were similar in style. Men's and women's clothing became very different from each other during the seventeenth century. By this time, the seamstress had become popular, making such things as *ruffs*, cravats and women's *negligé* clothes. Today, men's and women's clothing is again of similar design.

Designing fashion

Fashion design is at its most effective when the style suits the person wearing the clothes. Before beginning a design, the designer should consider the following questions:

- Where will it be worn?
- What season is it for?
- Which fabric will be used?
- What are the wearer's age and personality?

A new season's fashion is made up of styles adapted from the past to suit today's lifestyle. By changing collars, necklines, bodices, skirts, sleeves and trousers, a new style is created.

Draping

A very early form of clothing consisted of a large rectangle of woven cloth wrapped around the body. The folds in the fabric produced a graceful appearance. This form of clothing required little technical skill, as no patterns or sewing were required.

The Greeks and Romans were among the first to use this method of clothing.

The Greeks

The Greeks used wool or linen fabric and called their draped garment a *chiton*. There were two types of *chitons*, the *Doric* and the *Ionic*. Shape was achieved by the use of draping, girdles and pinning, and decoration included embroidered borders on the fabric. For outdoor wear, a wool *himation* was worn over the *chiton*. The method of draping this embroidered cloak was an art.

The Romans

At first the Romans made little change to the draped style developed by the Greeks. They did, however, change the names. The female garment became known as the *stola* and was often made of silk for the rich nobles, although wool and linen were the most common materials worn. For outdoor wear, a cloak or *palla* was added. Men wore a garment similar to the Greek *chiton*, known as a *tunica*.

Draping was a valued art. The method of draping later became a status symbol, indicating the wearer's social position. In time, a new style came into vogue, a type of tunic called a *dalmatica*, and draped garments began to be replaced by clothing cut to a pattern.

Greek Doric
Chiton of wool

Roman Tunica

Draped clothing of the ancient Greeks and Romans

Today, clothes are still designed using the technique of draping. Because it gives a graceful and elegant line, draping is used mainly for formal or evening wear. It is also a time-consuming technique, which means that it is unsuitable for mass production and is usually reserved for more expensive *couture* clothes.

Activities 1

(1) (a) Cut several rectangles of tissue paper or fabric 12 cm × 50 cm.

   (b) Referring to the illustrations of the *chiton* and *tunica*, fold the paper to copy the two styles. Use wool as a girdle where necessary.

   (c) Paste and label the models in your workbook.

(2) Using a long piece of lawn (or similar fabric) about 12 m long and a student volunteer, drape the fabric to represent a *palla*.

   (a) What problems did you need to overcome?

   (b) How difficult was it to maintain graceful folds?

   (c) Could the student move freely in the clothing?

Sleeves

The three main types of sleeves are *kimono*, *set-in* and *raglan*. These basic types can be varied to create interesting styles.

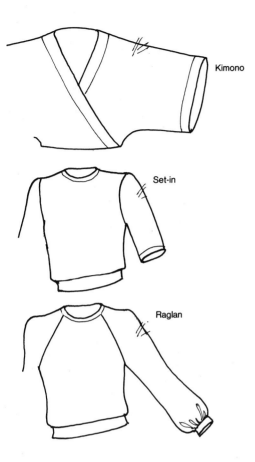

Kimono

Set-in

Raglan

Sleeves are sometimes designed to be made in different lengths.

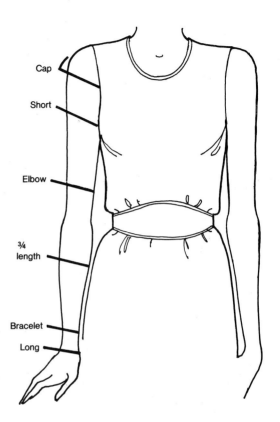

Cap

Short

Elbow

¾ length

Bracelet

Long

Look at the following sleeves. Which of the three basic sleeves has each developed from?

1

2

3

Sleeve styles have been taken to extremes. Look at the two costumes shown below. The woman's costume has large *leg of mutton* sleeves. The man's costume has very large *puffed sleeves*.

What do you think was done to make the sleeves keep their fullness?

Activity

(1) Collect illustrations of or draw 20 sleeve styles. The styles can be from any period in history.

(2) Paste them in your workbook, labelling each style.

1895 — Tailored costume for walking or sport, on navy linen with white braid trimming — white waistcoat & shirt blouse tie — gloves — blue straw hat — ribbons & plume

Man c. 1532 — black velvet gown with light fur trimming — black velvet jerkin & base — black hose & slashed shoes — crimson silk doublet, slashed on crest & sleeves to show white shirt, which is also visible at neck & wrists — grey sash — black cap — gold chain & medallion — dagger & tassel

Necklines and collars

Different combinations of neckline shapes and collar styles produce a huge variety of designs.

When choosing a collar or neckline, think about the garment's function. For example, is it to keep warm or is it for decoration?

A *collar* can be smart and tailored or soft and feminine. The basic collar styles are shown below.

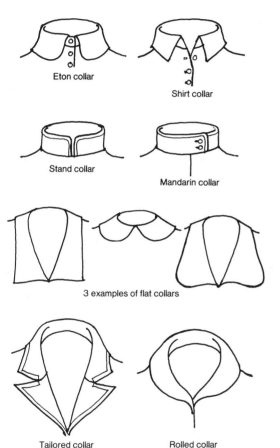

Eton collar

Shirt collar

Stand collar

Mandarin collar

3 examples of flat collars

Tailored collar

Rolled collar

Activity

Paste in your workbook:

(1) Ten illustrations of collars.
(2) A picture of a collar designed 100 years ago. How does it compare with collar styles today?

Some *necklines* need collars, while others do not. Here are some examples of necklines that do not need collars:

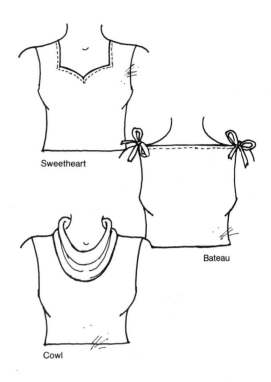

Sweetheart

Bateau

Cowl

Activity

In your workbook, draw examples of necklines that are often worn today.

Shape and fit

If a garment is to fit the body, the fabric must be shaped. This is particularly important in the case of woven fabrics.

Fabric can be shaped to fit the body by the use of darts, seams, gathers, tucks, folds and yokes.

Darts — May be in six positions:

1 Shoulder	4 Neckline
2 Underarm	5 Centre front line
3 Waist	6 In seams

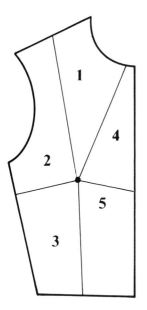

Six possible ways to spread fullness for a bodice

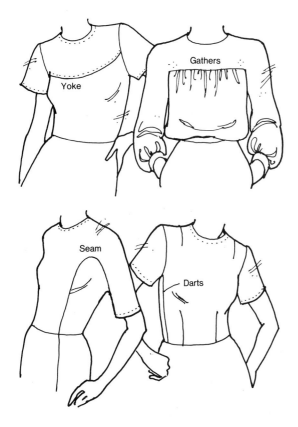

Seams — Shape is achieved by putting fullness in the seam. Used when a dart would not suit a design.

Gathers — Fabric is pulled up to produce fullness instead of using a dart.

Tucks — Fabric is tucked at regular intervals. Tucks may be small (pintucks) or up to 1 cm wide.

Folds — Tucks larger than 1 cm are considered to be folded as in unpressed pleats.

Yokes — Control fullness, giving a neat appearance.

Activity

Collect illustrations of garments with no darts, where the fullness is controlled by the methods listed above, and paste them in your workbook.

Trousers

Trousers are worn by men and women and are also referred to as slacks. There are five basic styles, to suit the needs of people in different parts of the world.

Activity

Find out what style of trousers is worn by people in three countries other than Australia.

(1) Draw each style in your workbook.
(2) Describe each style in approximately half a page.

Fashion detail

Fashion detailing involves drawing designs and showing such details as pleating, fullness and tailoring. Shown opposite are examples of sketches showing pleats, skirt fullness, pocket detailing and plackets (openings at the neck, sleeve or waist).

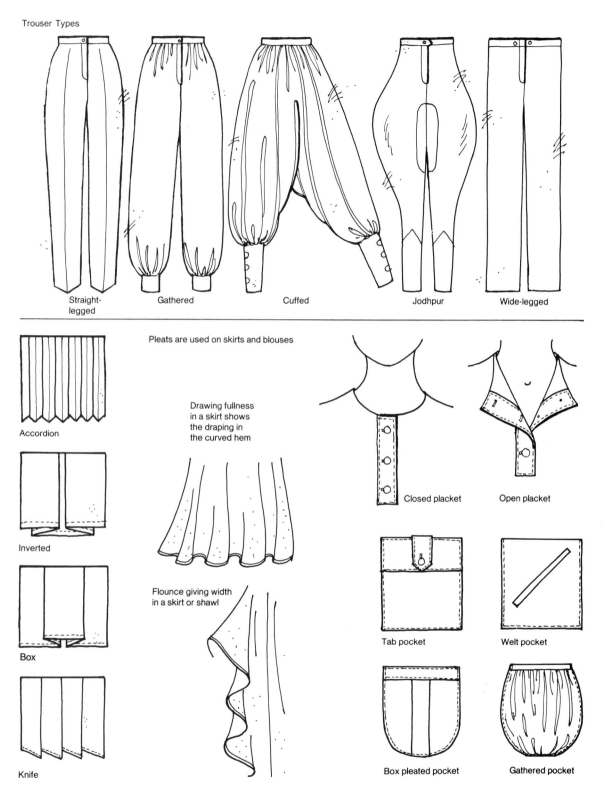

Trouser Types

Straight-legged

Gathered

Cuffed

Jodhpur

Wide-legged

Accordion

Inverted

Box

Knife

Pleats are used on skirts and blouses

Drawing fullness in a skirt shows the draping in the curved hem

Flounce giving width in a skirt or shawl

Closed placket

Open placket

Tab pocket

Welt pocket

Box pleated pocket

Gathered pocket

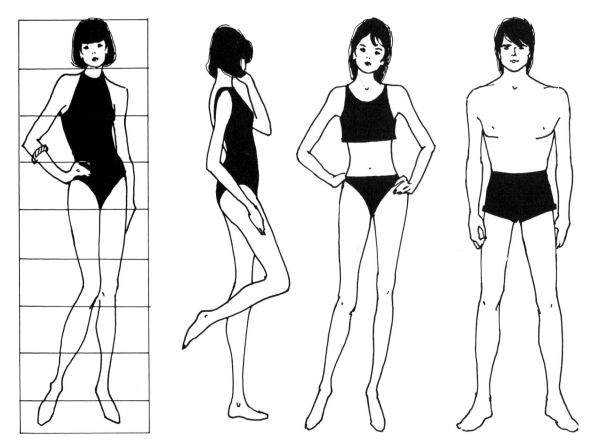

Trace the figures to use as models for the following design activities.

Activities

(1) Using the figure outlines shown, design the following styles in your workbook.

• Tennis clothing • Beach wear • New school uniform • Outfit suitable to wear for a job interview • Shirt • Summer trousers or shorts

(2) As a clothing designer you have been asked to design a set of three articles suitable for casual wear by teenagers in summer. The articles can be for boys or girls.

(a) Design the clothes, using the figure outlines shown.

(b) Select suitable fabric and attach a 5 cm × 5 cm sample of each.
(c) Give reasons for your choice of fabric.
(d) Label your style with design details.

Basic design

There are both *elements* and *principles* of design. When these are heeded, a design will be *aesthetically* pleasing.

Design consists of:
• Line and direction
• Shape and proportion
• Colour
• Texture.

Line and direction

The *line* of a garment gives our eyes a *direction* to follow. Lines may be horizontal, vertical, oblique or curved. The direction of a line can help create an *illusion*. For instance, horizontal lines can make a person appear wider than he or she really is, because the eye follows the lines across the person.

Activity

Look at the lines on the clothing illustrated.
(1) What effect do the following lines have on clothing?
    (a) Vertical
    (b) Horizontal
(2) What type of build should a person have to look good in wide horizontal lines?

Horizontal   Vertical   Diagonal   Curved

Which garment shapes fit the fashion silhouettes above?

Shape and proportion

The *shape* of garments changes with fashion. Shape gives the *silhouette* of the clothing. A silhouette or outline changes the *proportions* of the clothing.

Above are some basic garment shapes. These shapes determine the silhouette, which often distinguishes one costume period from another.

Activity

(1) Draw the silhouettes shown above in your workbook.
(2) Research the silhouette of clothing during the last ten years.
(3) What change do you notice in the silhouette? Why do you think this change has occurred?

Good *proportion* is achieved when the various sections of a garment relate well to the whole garment. Different proportions suit different figures.

Activity

Look at the proportions of the three shirts shown on page 87. Which shirt is better proportioned? Give reasons for your choice.

Texture

Texture is an important design element. The texture or surface of the fabric may be shiny like satin, dull and soft like velvet, rough and bulky like some wool or filmy and transparent like chiffon.

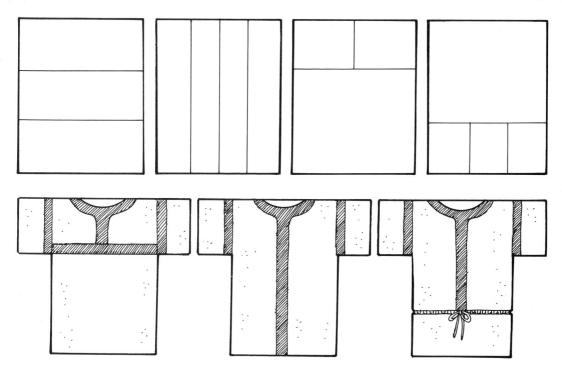

Activity

(1) Between the class, collect thirty samples of fabrics.
(2) Describe the samples, e.g. rough, shiny, smooth.
(3) Group the fabrics under these headings on the noticeboard.
(4) Each class member is to select one fabric that appeals to him or her and design a suitable article of clothing.

Colour

Colour can affect our emotions and moods. Bright colours such as red and yellow are happy and exciting, while blues and greens are cool and serene. Black and grey are sombre and, to some people, depressing.

When choosing a colour, you need to consider your hair and skin colour. Colour also affects your figure shape. Dark colours tend to 'retreat' and so make people look smaller, while brighter colours can make you look big-

Colours, line, pattern and shape create the design of clothes.

ger. Use this to advantage. If you have big hips, choose cool colours for trousers and skirts.

Colours vary from light to dark. This is known as the *tone* or *value* of colours.

Choosing a pattern

Before deciding on a pattern or style, analyse your figure carefully so as to minimise your faults and take advantage of your good points.

Figure	Line	Colour	Design	Fabric
Short	• Vertical lines • Stripes	• One colour • Separates	• Raised waistlines • Detail at necklines • Straight-legged trousers	• Plain textures • Small prints • Soft fabrics
Tall	• Horizontal • Yokes and belts • Pockets	• Contrasting • Colours in separates	• Waist or hipline interest • Detail on styles • Flared and cuffed trousers	• Bulky textures • Plaids, checks, stripes, florals • Soft and crisp fabrics
Slim	• Horizontal and curved • Rounded silhouettes	• Light, bright colours	• Collars, scarves • Full sleeves • Fashion detail such as intricate pockets, plackets, pleating • Wide-legged trousers	• Textured plaids and prints
Big build	• Vertical • Easy-fitting silhouettes	• Dark, cool colours • One-colour outfits	• Simple A-line style • Soft self-fabric belts	• Simple, plain textures • Medium prints • Crisp fabrics
Bottom heavy	• Vertical or horizontal in upper area • Yokes, gathers, tucks	• Contrasting colours • Bright prints and patterns on tops	• Neckline interest • Upper pockets • Long jackets • Slimming dresses better than trousers	• Simple texture for skirts or trousers • Texture fabric for tops only
Top heavy	• Vertical • Horizontal in hip area	• Contrast with darker colours for tops	• Asymmetrical closures • Uncluttered upper silhouettes	• Simple, lightweight • Plain textures for tops

Activities

(1) *Fashion quiz*

Answer true or false to the following:

(1) A short person should not wear clothes with horizontal lines. _____

(2) Overweight short people should wear garments with big checks. _____

(3) Tall slim people can wear bright floral clothing. _____

(4) A top-heavy person should not wear shirts with yokes and soft gathering. _____

(5) A mohair jumper will make a chubby person look slimmer. _____

(6) Brightly coloured, checked cowboy shirts will suit tall slim people. _____

(7) Heavy-hipped people should wear brightly coloured trousers. _____

(8) Black satin evening trousers would suit a person with an average figure. _____

(9) Stretch jeans would suit a heavy-hipped person. _____

(10) A-line styles are most suitable for the generous figure. _____

(2) *Fashion crossword*

Across

1 Outline shape of a garment (10)
2 Technique of clothing that requires no pattern or sewing (5)
3 The fit of a garment is improved by using (5)
4 Type of trousers (7)
5 Type of collar (8)
6 Fabric with a smooth shiny surface (5)
7 Slimming line that adds height (8)
8 Basic sleeve (6)

Down

1 Type of pleat (9)
2 Line that adds width (10)
3 Quiet receding colour (4)
4 The surface of a fabric is referred to as — (7)
5 Bright, bold colour (3)
6 Method used to make a sleeve appear fuller (7)
7 Garment shape can affect the ____ of a style (10)

Words to remember

cissorii	leg-of-mutton
ruffs	jodhpurs
negligé	element
drape	principles
chiton	aesthetically
Doric	line
Ionic	direction
stola	proportion
palla	illusion
tunica	shape
dalmatica	silhouette
couture	texture

Extension activities

(1) (a) Describe how you would make a garment by the draping method.
   (b) Find an illustration of or draw a draped garment that would be worn today.

(2) Design a garment for an elderly person. Describe in half a page the basic design features you considered in designing the garment.

Glossary

Chiton — Greek name for garment made from a draped rectangle of fabric.
Drape — To wrap or fold fabric around the body in graceful folds.
Leg-of-mutton — Very full sleeve, often requiring padding at the top, narrowing to a closely fitting sleeve from elbow to wrist.
Jodhpurs — A type of trousers that fit tightly from the knee to the ankle, worn for horse-riding.

Further reading

Gostelow, M. *Dress Sense*, Batsford, 1985

Ireland, P. *Fashion Design*, Cambridge University Press, Sydney, 1981

Ireland, P. *Fashion Design Drawing*, Batsford, London, 1970

Ireland, P. *Fashion Drawing*, Cambridge University Press, Sydney, 1980

Simplicity Sewing Book, Simplicity Patterns, London, 1975

8

Choosing and making clothes

Clothing is our outer covering. It can also be a comment on the type of person we are. Consider the following descriptions — do one or more of these describe you?

- Neat and tidy
- Well co-ordinated
- Respectable
- Scruffy
- Comfortably dressed
- Follower of fashion
- Easy going
- Sophisticated
- Conform to peer group
- Fashion innovator
- Imaginative

The *image* a person creates depends partly on clothing. It is a good idea to consider carefully the contribution a new article of clothing will make to your appearance. Remember that you will get the most use from clothes you feel comfortable in. Clothes often express the type of person you are.

When choosing clothes (whether you are buying or making them), you need to consider the following: your personality, your physical features, your lifestyle, your resources and your budget. We shall look at each of these in turn.

Personality

Everyone is different. The following words describe types of personalities:

- Shy
- Outgoing
- Happy
- Quiet
- Extrovert
- Introvert
- Moody
- Talkative
- Bright
- Confident

Think about yourself and your friends. How would you describe your own and your friends' personalities?

Have you noticed that outgoing people often dress in bright colours and unusual styles? Quiet people may dress in *subdued* or *sombre* colours such as brown and green. These sombre colours do not draw attention to the wearer. Very confident people often wear exaggerated or very modern clothes. They are not afraid to wear clothes that are different. Most people wear the same type of clothes as the people in their peer group.

Activity

(1) How would you describe your personality? Think carefully; discuss it with your friends.

(2) Write a paragraph on your personality and the type of clothes you enjoy wearing.

Physical features

Face and hair

The colour of your eyes, skin and hair combine to create your colouring. Your colouring largely determines the colours that suit you.

Your face shape will determine the most suitable hair style and neckline for you. When these complement each other, there is greater fashion impact.

Activity

(1) What shape face have you got?
(2) Look at a current fashion magazine and sketch necklines and collars that would suit you.

Body shape

People describe body type in relation to height and weight, for example 'tall and thin', 'short and fat', 'top heavy' or 'bottom heavy'.

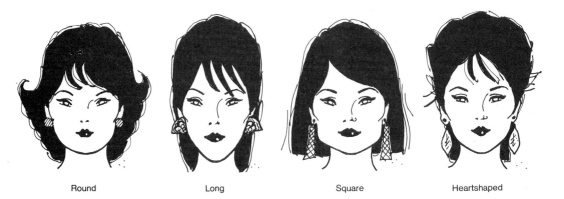

Round   Long   Square   Heartshaped

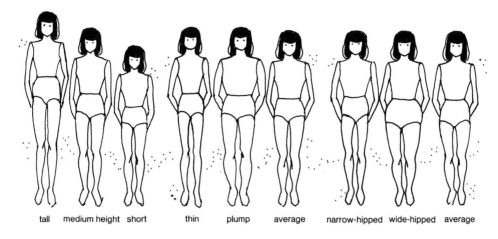

tall   medium height short   thin   plump   average   narrow-hipped wide-hipped average

Various body shapes

Lifestyle

The term *lifestyle* refers to the type of activities people are involved in during their life. From time to time, of course, people may change their activities and therefore their lifestyle.

Your lifestyle may include some of the following activities:
- Sports — such as football, netball, tennis and archery
- Dancing
- Painting
- Stamp collecting
- Films

The clothes you choose to wear must be suitable for the activities that are part of your lifestyle. Today, people tend to dress casually. There is a need, however, to have some good clothing for special occasions, such as a party, dance or wedding, which may arise unexpectedly.

Some of the other things that affect your lifestyle are:
- *Climate* — Clothes must suit the season. People who live in hot climates tend to dress more casually.
- *Community* — People in the country often dress differently from people in the city.
- *Family activities* — Some families go on a lot of picnics; others often eat out at restaurants.

Resources

Some people have more resources than others. If you identify your own resources, you will be able to use them wisely.

Resources include:

- *Money* — Influences the quality and quantity you can buy.
- *Skills* — The ability to sew gives you access to a greater range of clothes for less cost.
- *Knowledge* — Knowing which clothes suit your figure and personality.
- *Interest* — Affects the time you give to planning your clothes and accessories.

Budget

Following these four steps will help you to manage your money wisely:

(1) Estimate how much you have to spend.
(2) Prepare a list of the clothing and accessories you have that you can wear again this season.
(3) List the clothes you will need to buy.
(4) Think about the clothes you could make to save money. Make a list.

To help you plan your clothing needs, draw up a chart like the following:

Activities you participate in	Clothes you already have	Clothes you need (buy/make)

Be wise, and work out how much you can spend on each item before you buy clothes or fabric. This will stop you overspending on one item and so being unable to buy the other things you need.

Making your own clothes

Body measurements

Before buying a pattern, you need to know your correct size.

Take your measurements before buying a pattern — it's the first step to making a successful garment! This chart will help. Update it frequently, just in case your figure has changed enough to need a different pattern size. Measurements #1-#5 below are the body measurements on which your pattern type and size are based. Compare these with the measurements on the size charts in the pattern catalogue before deciding on your type and size.

If possible, have someone help you measure. Before you begin, tie a string snugly around your natural waistline. When you're taking the measurements, this will clearly define your waistline position.

HOW TO MEASURE	YOUR BODY MEASUREMENTS
1. BUST/CHEST around the fullest part	
2. HIGH BUST (girls) directly under arms, above bust **NECK (boys)** at base	
3. WAIST over the string	
4. HIPS at these distances below waist: **14–18 cm–Girls;** 15 cm–Boys; 18 cm–Young Junior/ Teen, Teen–Boys, Half-Size; 20.5 cm–Men; **23 cm–Misses, Women.**	
5. BACK WAIST LENGTH from prominent bone at back neck base to waist	

HOW TO MEASURE	YOUR BODY MEASUREMENTS
6. FRONT WAIST LENGTH from shoulder at neck base to waist (over bust point on girls)	
7. SHOULDER TO BUST (girls) from shoulder at neck base to bust point	
8. SHOULDER LENGTH from neck base to shoulder bone	
9. BACK WIDTH across back, at these distances below neck base: **10 cm–Girls, Boys;** 11.5 cm–Young Junior/ Teen, Teen–Boys; **12.5 cm–Misses, Women, Half-Size;** 15 cm–Men.	
10. ARM LENGTH from shoulder bone to wrist-bone, over slightly bent elbow	
11. SHOULDER TO ELBOW (girls) from end of shoulder to middle of slightly bent elbow	
12. UPPER ARM around arm at fullest part between shoulder and elbow	
13. CROTCH DEPTH from side waist to chair (sit on a flat chair and use a ruler)	
14. CROTCH LENGTH from centre back waist between the legs to centre front waist	
15. THIGH around fullest part	
16. BACK SKIRT LENGTH (girls) from centre back at waist to desired length	
17. PANTS SIDE LENGTH from side waistline to desired length along outside of leg	

Commercial patterns

Commercial patterns are mass produced so that people can make their own fashionable clothes without the need to *draft* a pattern. Accessories can be added to give an individual look. Changes to a pattern style can also add variety; for example, changing the collar or sleeve length or adding decorative features such as buttons, pockets and frills.

All patterns are designed from *basic blocks*. A basic block pattern fits the body but has no style or decoration. By using basic blocks for skirts, sleeves and bodices, you can design any style you choose.

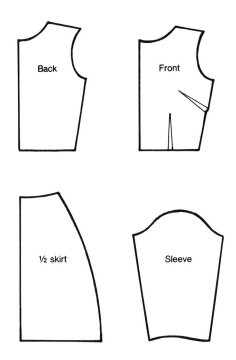

Activities

(1) All pattern companies use basically the same markings and instructions on their pattern pieces. Referring to a commercial pattern, choose the correct name of each of the labelled pattern markings from the chart on the next page.

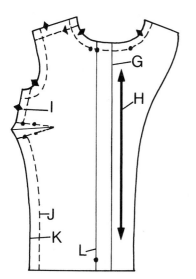
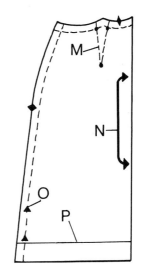

Part	Pattern marking			
	A	**B**	**C**	**D**
G	Button extension	Straight grain	Stitching line	Place on fold
H	Direction of sewing indicator	Centre front line	Straight grain	Notch
I	Dart	Notch	Place on fold	Straight grain
J	Stitching line	Cutting line	Straight grain	Button extension
K	Button extension	Place on fold	Stitching line	Cutting line
L	Place on fold	Hem line	Button extension	Centre front line
M	Dart	Button extension	Direction of sewing indicator	Notch
N	Direction of sewing indicator	Place on fold	Dart	Stitching line
O	Notch	Direction of sewing indicator	Dart	Cutting line
P	Place on fold	Cutting line	Hem line	Stitching line

(2) Draw the pattern pieces needed to make this article.

(3) Select the pattern pieces needed to make this coat.

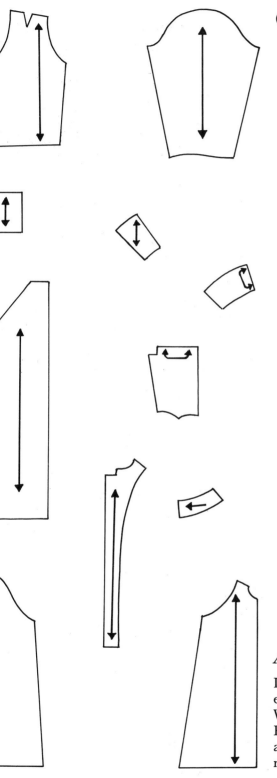

(4) Draw and label fully the pattern pieces needed to make this shirt.

Adjusting patterns

It is sometimes necessary to adjust a pattern, even though you have bought the correct size. We are all built somewhat differently, after all. Before you start to sew, pin the pieces together and try the garment on. Minor changes can be made at this stage and will save time later.

the Problem   **the Solution**

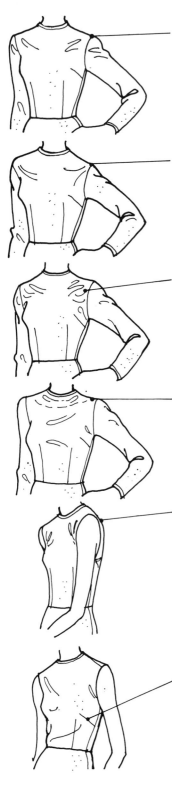

Broad Shoulders
The garment will pull across chest, back and top of sleeves.

Remove sleeve; take new fitting line out to edge at shoulders, adding up to 1 cm on shoulder width (taken from seam allowance). Reset sleeve.

Narrow Shoulders
Sleeve seams will fall off shoulders.

Remove sleeve and make a new fitting line at top of armhole, taking out excess width at shoulder. Trim garment seam allowance to 1.5 cm. Reset sleeve.

Sloping Shoulders
Fullness will show around the armhole and shoulder. Pick up and pin excess at shoulder, tapering to nothing at neck. Lower armhole the same amount as removed at shoulder. Slightly sloping shoulders can be improved by using shaped shoulder pads.

Square Shoulders
Fullness appears around neck and across bust. Rip shoulders, add up to 1 cm to shoulder edges at armhole. Pin out excess at neck edge. Raise armhole the same amount as added at shoulder.

Round Shoulders
Back bodice pulls above waistline; fullness shows at back armhole and front shoulder. Rip shoulders, shoulder dart and waistline seam. Lift excess fabric at back and front and bring it into shoulder seam and shoulder dart, taking up to 1 cm from armhole seam allowance. Repin armhole. Drop back neckline; add up to 1 cm at back waistline. Raise front waistline accordingly.

Raising or Lowering the Bust Dart
Bust darts will not point to bust; they will be too low or too high.

Rip side seams; repin dart higher or lower, parallel to original dart; repin side seam.

the Problem   **the Solution**

Small Bust

Fullness appears at bustline due to the darts being too deep.

Rip side seams, waistline seam and underarm darts. (It may also be necessary to rip waistline darts.) Repin smaller darts. Increase side and waistline seams.

Full Bust

Tightness will occur across bust and back. Waist will probably rise at sides.

Rip side seams, waistline seam and underarm darts. (It may also be necessary to rip waistline darts.) Pin deeper darts. Decrease side and waistline seams.

Full Neck

Neckline will be tight, and will pull and wrinkle. Clip neckline carefully as shown until it sets properly. Mark new neckline. Remember to correct neckline facing, too.

High Hip

Dress will appear shorter on one side; centre of skirt will shoot off at an angle.

Release waist edges and drop skirt on "high hip" side until hem is parallel to floor — up to 1 cm. More length than this must be adjusted on the pattern before cutting.

Large Hips

Tightness and wrinkles around hips.

Add the needed width equally at the side seams. Taper to waistline or increase waistline darts the amount added at side seams, returning waistline to original size.

Sway Back

Wrinkles or excess fabric appear above and below waist at back of skirt.

Rip waist. Repin, taking up excess fabric from bodice and skirt waistlines. Refit darts, if necessary, to follow body contour.

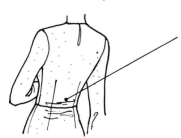

the Problem   **the Solution**

Large Waist
Not enough ease at waistline to fit comfortably. Wrinkles above and below the waist.

Decrease size of darts and let out side seams between bust and hips.

Small Waist
Excess fabric at waistline. Natural waistline is not evident.

Increase size of darts and take in side seams between bust and hips.

Large Abdomen
Front of skirt pulls across abdomen. Waistline and hem curve up at centre front.

Rip waist seam, darts and side seams. Lower skirt at front until hem is even. Fit side seams and darts to body contour.

Large Derrière
Back of skirt wrinkles and tends to ride up at centre back. Side seams are pulled toward the back.

Rip waist seam, darts and side seams. Lower skirt at back until hem is even. Fit side seams and darts to body contour.

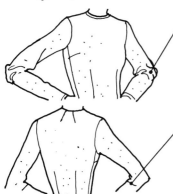

Full Upper Arm
Tightness and drawing across upper arm; not enough ease to swing arm freely.

Let out sleeve seam allowance to 1 cm from armhole edge, tapering to the normal seam allowance at elbow.

Large Elbow
Tightness and wrinkles at elbow only.

Pull out back seam allowance at elbow, keeping 1.5 cm seam allowance at top and wrist, tapering to 6 mm at elbow.

Elbow Dart
The dart should be at the point of the elbow.

Rip dart and sleeve seam. Measure up or down from point of dart the amount needed to make it fit properly; pin in new dart.

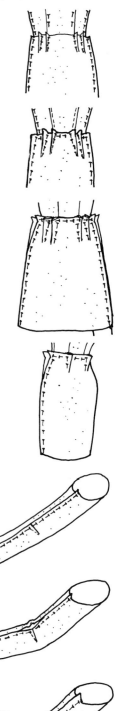

What if the jacket length needs to be adjusted?

Here's what to do

- Measure the man at the centre back from base of neck to desired finished length of jacket
- Compare his measurement to the finished length of the jacket on the back of the pattern envelope
- Measure the back pattern piece at the centre back to the waistline
- Compare this measurement to the back waist length on the Men's Measurement chart
- If the waistline is in the right place, adjust the pattern below the waist. If the waistline is higher or lower than it should be, adjust the pattern above the waist. In some cases it is necessary to adjust both above and below the waist
- Use the Easy-Rule guide to lengthen or shorten as previously explained
- When there is no Easy-Rule Guide, draw a line across each pattern piece at right angles to the grain line
- To lengthen, cut all the pieces along the drawn line and separate them the necessary amount

- Tape in place over tissue paper and check to be sure that grain lines are straight
- To shorten, draw a second line parallel to the first line on each pattern piece. The distance between the lines is the amount of adjustment
- Fold the bottom line up to meet the top line and tape adjustment in place
- For both methods, adjust all related pieces — front, back, side, interfacing, facing and lining
- Correct the cutting lines where necessary
- Respace buttonholes and reposition pockets if affected

What if the pants wrinkle in back between waist and derrière?

Here's what to do

- Crotch is too long in back. Check Men's Measurement chart for amount of adjustment
- Shorten the crotch the necessary amount as illustrated
- New cutting lines will taper down to inseam cutting line and up to centre back cutting line

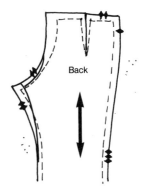

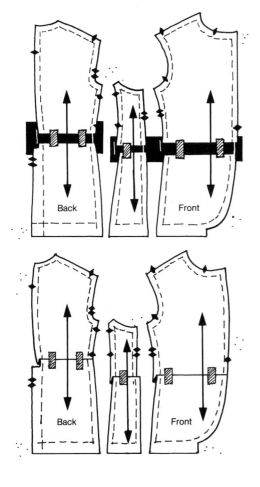

What if the inseam length needs to be adjusted?

Here's what to do

- Check Men's Measurement chart for the amount of adjustment
- To lengthen, use the Easy-Rule Guide between crotch and hem. Cut pattern apart on the dotted line
- Using the printed ruler as a guide, spread the pattern pieces the necessary amount
- Tape in place over tissue paper
- To shorten, crease the pattern at the base line of the Easy-Rule Guide and fold a pleat taking up the necessary amount
- Tape pleat in place

What if the pants are too tight through the thigh?

Here's what to do

- Check Men's Measurement chart for the amount of adjustment
- Tape tissue paper under the pants front and back in the thigh area
- Divide the total amount of adjustment by four and increase inseams and side seams this amount at the biggest part of the thigh
- On the inseam draw a new cutting line, tapering up to the crotch cutting line and down to the knee area
- On the side seam draw a new cutting line, tapering up to the hip cutting line and down to the knee area

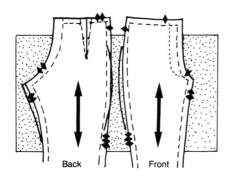

Back　　　Front

What if the waistline has to be adjusted?

Here's what to do

- Check the Men's Measurement chart for amount of adjustment
- The centre back seam on a man's pattern can be increased 5 cm without increasing the pattern because of the extra seam allowance at centre back
- If the adjustment is more than 5 cm add to the centre back and to the waistbands

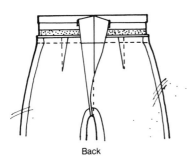

Back

Choosing fabric

Having decided on a pattern, you will need to choose a fabric. There is a very wide range of fabrics to choose from. Begin by asking youself a few questions:

- How much can I afford to spend?
- How long do I want the garment to last?
- What care will the fabric need?
- Will the fabric suit the season?
- Will the fabric suit the style?

Note: Read the back of the pattern envelope to see which fabrics are most suitable for the style you have chosen.

The fabric you select may be a *fibre blend*. The advantages of blends include:

- The best qualities of each fibre are kept.
- They are often cheaper than pure fabrics.
- They offer a greater variety of surface decorations.

Blending

Blending is done during one of the four stages of fibre production:

(1) Breaking and opening bundles of fibres delivered to the factory
(2) Carding
(3) Combing fibres
(4) Drawing out yarns.

Many fibres can be blended together. The following are the most common blends for everyday use.

- *Polyester and cotton* — Polyester reduces creasing, which the cotton fibre is prone to, and thereby improves performance.
- *Rayon and acetate* — These fibres are blended mainly to improve appearance.
- *Nylon, polyester and acrylics* — These are all *synthetics* that will improve durability.
- *Nylon and polyester* — When added to acetate or wool, these fibres result in a stronger yarn and improve wrinkle resistance.

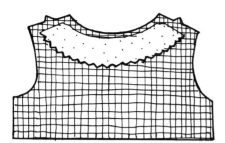

Sewing techniques

Commercial patterns tell you how to sew the article. The following will help give your sewing an individual touch.

Interfacing

Fusible (iron-on) interfacing saves time. Test first on a small sample of fabric. Pink the edges not to be sewn. Apply directly to the wrong side.

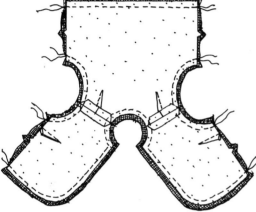

Lining

This method is suitable for sleeveless garments.

- Cut 3 mm on all lining edges except shoulder and side seams.
- Sew darts.
- Sew shoulder seams.
- Press.
- Put right sides together and sew lining to garment, leaving side seams open.
- Turn right side out.

- With right sides together, sew garment together at sides.
- Machine end of lining 2–3 cm. Turn rest of lining edge inside out and slip stitch down seam line.

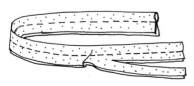

Bound buttonholes

Quick method for firm fabrics.

- Cut a strip 2.5 cm wide and long enough to make buttonholes needed.
- Fold strip in half lengthwise and machine 3 mm from folded edge.

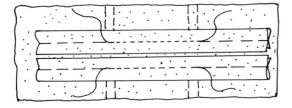

- Trim raw edges, and cut strips into sections.
  For each strip:
- Baste to right side. Place raw edge on buttonhole and extend ends 1.3 cm.
- Sew over previous stitching the length of buttonhole.
- Do not reverse the stitch. Tie ends off.

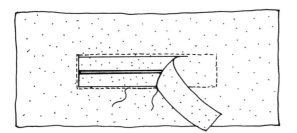

- Cut buttonhole line and turn strips to wrong side. Press.

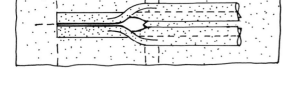

- Pin facing in place.
- Tack.
- Hand stitch.

- On facing side, cut fabric close to stitching.

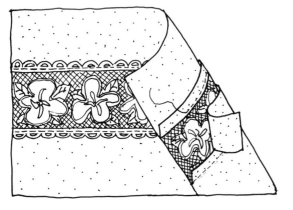

Lace inserts
Fabric must be flat with no curves.
- Select lace 1.5–10 cm wide.
- Pin lace in position and then tack in place.
- Top stitch close to edge.
- On wrong side, cut fabric down centre of lace insert.

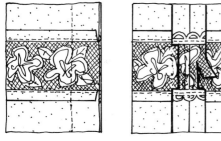

- Trim to size.
- Fold raw edges under and, using small stitches, slip stitch the edges either side of the lace carefully.

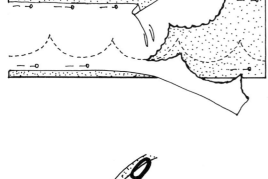

Scallops
Some dressmakers' rulers are scalloped. You can draw your own scallop pattern on paper.

An edge to be scalloped should be 5 cm deeper than the scallop required.

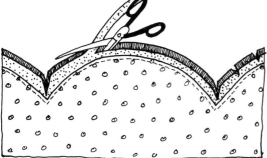

- Tack facing pattern over facing.
- Sew along scalloped line through all fabric thicknesses, using a small stitch.
- After sewing, remove paper carefully.

- Interfacing, if used, should be trimmed close to seam.
- Trim and clip fabric to obtain a good curve.

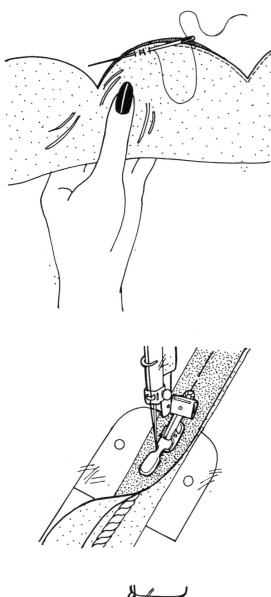

- Turn facing to wrong side.
- Press first on facing side, then on front of article.
- Understitching prevents fabric rolling to front. Use small running stitches on the *wrong* side.

Cording
Cording can be bought in various thicknesses.
- Cut fabric on the bias.
- Keep right sides out.
- Use a zipper foot and machine cord in place.
- Stretch bias slightly as you sew.

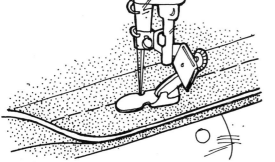

- Machine baste cording on the right side of a single seam.
- When in position, sew into place using an average-sized stitch.

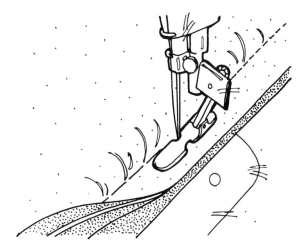

- Now place garment sections together. The basting stitch of the cording section can be used as a guide to sewing.

Button loops

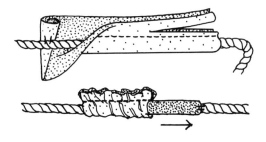

Fabric loops
- Cut bias strip 2.8 cm wide.
- Fold strips in half lengthwise, with right sides together.
- Sew 6 cm from fold, slanting the stitching at one end.
- Use a tapestry needle to turn inside out. Attach thread to one end and turn right side out.

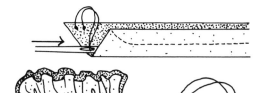

Corded loops
A cord is sometimes inserted into a loop to add strength and increase thickness.

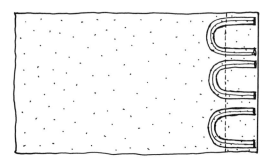

Attaching loops (1)
Use cut loops for large buttons or when loops are placed some distance apart.
- On right side of fabric, machine baste loops on the seam allowance.
- With right sides together, pin facing over loops.
- With garment side uppermost, sew sections together, using the first line of stitching as a guide.

- Trim to reduce bulk in seam. Fold facing to inside on seamline. Press.

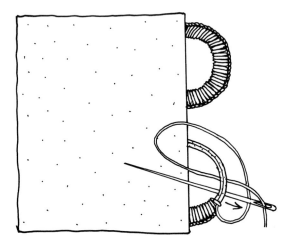

Attaching loops (2)
Used for small buttons placed close together.
- First sew a long strip using previous method.
- Draw a grid on a sheet of paper and form loops by shaping the strip into a line of C's.
- Machine onto paper.
- Place paper with loops onto fabric. Carefully position machine. Remove paper.
- Add facing, using method given in (1).

Thread loops
Quick, easy method suitable for small buttons.
- Mark position of loops on the edge of the garment *opposite* the buttons.
- Sew 5 strands of thread through buttonholes. Check that buttons can pass through.
- Loop stitch over thread strands. Secure firmly on back of facing with very small double stitch.

Words to remember

image	draft
subdued	basic blocks
sombre	blend
peer group	management
lifestyle	

Revision exercises

(1) Explain how a peer group can influence the clothes people wear.
(2) What effect does lifestyle have on the clothing people buy?
(3) List ways in which you can add variety and style to a commercial pattern to make it more individual.
(4) Would you choose a shirt made of a cotton-polyester blend in preference to one made of 100 per cent cotton? Give your reasons.

Extension activities

(1) *Wardrobe consultant*
As a wardrobe consultant you help people select clothes that suit their lifestyles.

(a) Compile a portfolio of clothing suitable for a young executive in a law firm. The person is 25 years old and can be male or female. Money is not a problem.
(b) Divide your portfolio into sections:
(a) Office wear
(b) Evening wear
(c) Casual or weekend wear.
Explain your clothing choices for each section.

(2) *Clothing wonderword*

clothes	colour
peer	body
group	money
fashion	skill
image	knowledge
personality	commercial
resources	subdued
budget	draft
occasions	sport
casual	blocks

Complete the following sentence with the left-over letters:

___ ___ ____ _____ __ ____ ____ _____.

```
K N O W L E D G E C S B U B
Y C O L O U R R A A U L C L
L Y O U R C A O L S B O L O
N O I H S A F U T U D H O C
S C M I N G T P T A U O T K
K C A S U S E I T L E Y H S
I A G O U E P R B U D G E T
L S E Y R E S O U R C E S P
L I D C O M M E R C I A L E
M O N E Y R S O N T A L I T
B N P E R S O N A L I T Y Y
```

Glossary

Image — The idea of yourself you project through your appearance and behaviour.
Peer group — A group of people similar to you in some respect (e.g. of the same age or belonging to the same club or interest group).

Draft — To draw a pattern, using body measurements.

Further reading

Butler, M. *Clothes: Their Choosing, Making and Care*, Batsford, 1975

9

Theatre design

For this unit you need:

- Your imagination
- All cast-off clothing and accessories you can find
- Any odds and ends that could be converted into part of a costume.

Before designing costumes for a drama or musical, the designer needs to understand the story and its setting.

Before beginning a theatre design, answer these questions:

- In what period is the play set?
- What is the mood of the play?
- What are the personalities and ages of the characters?
- What clothing styles were worn during the period?
- What types of accessories or decoration did people wear?
- What fabrics and textiles were available?
- What will the stage setting be?
- What colours would be most suitable for the stage presentation?

Colour choice will depend on the atmosphere to be created by a particular scene and the various characters. For example, black may be chosen for an 'evil' character and white to suggest innocence. Generally, bright and contrasting colours are used on stage to attract the audience's attention to the actors. Such colours also make the actors stand out from the surrounding scenery.

Choosing fabrics

Once the style of the costume has been decided, it is time to choose the fabric.

The amount of money available will largely determine the fabrics you choose. Fabrics should be *durable* but inexpensive. To ensure an *authentic* looking costume, the fabric must be easily adaptable to the period the play is set in. Remember, the fabrics you select help to create the illusion on stage.

Furnishing fabrics have advantages for the costume designer, because they are often less expensive and generally wider than dress fabrics. However, furnishing fabric is usually heavier than dress fabric, so check that the drape is suitable for the style.

Making theatre costumes

Theatre costumes must be able to withstand actors changing quickly from one costume to another between scenes. At the same time they must keep a good appearance.

Traditional sewing techniques are less important for theatrical garments than sturdy construction. You will find the following techniques useful:

- Neaten raw edges of seams if you suspect they will fray.
- Zig-zag the seams of knit fabrics to allow for give.

- Machine hems where necessary.
- *Selvedges* provide an edge that needs no further machining.

Fabrics for theatre costumes

Below is a list of fabrics that are suitable for making theatrical costumes. Refer to this list when designing clothes for the activities at the end of this chapter.

Calico

Plain-weave cotton cloth with a smooth surface. Calico may be bleached or unbleached and can be bought in different weights. It has poor drape but is ideal for dyeing and printing.

Canvas

A strong, heavy, plain-weave fabric, also known as duck or sailcloth (which are slightly lighter in weight). Originally made of cotton, it may now contain some synthetic fibres. Good for interlinings for period bodices that need rigid lines.

Challis

A soft, lightweight, plain-weave fabric. May be made from wool or cotton, although wool challis is not as suitable for costume design, being a fairly expensive fabric.

Chiffon

Very soft, flimsy, very lightweight material with outstanding drape. May be made from various fibres, nylon and polyesters being the cheapest. Synthetic chiffon has the disadvantage of being stiff, but this can be overcome temporarily by soaking it in a solution of fabric softener.

Corduroy

A ribbed-pile fabric made of cotton or polyester and cotton. Although appropriate only for twentieth-century styles, it has the advantages of being inexpensive and durable.

Crepe

Crepe describes a crinkled surface finish on fabrics that is achieved by the use of high twisting yarns, special weaving or a chemical process. Synthetic crepes are inexpensive and are ideal for full or bias-cut skirts.

Crepe de Chine

Originally made from silk but now available in less expensive synthetic forms, such as rayon and acetate. Suitable for linings and also romantic-style skirts, dresses and nightwear.

Denim

A twill-weave fabric made of cotton or cotton and polyester. Has poor drape but can be softened by washing. Traditional denim is dark coloured and obviously has limited use for period costume.

Drill

A twill-weave of better quality and appearance than denim. Available colours include white and khaki. The best drill is made from cotton. Used for uniforms, jackets and tropical wear. Because of its poor drape, it is most suitable for tailored clothing.

Fibreglass

Suitable only for interior design use, such as curtains, as it can irritate the skin.

Flannel

A soft, plain-weave fabric made of wool. Traditionally used for men's trousers.

Flannelette

A cotton version of flannel, with a nap (a soft, fuzzy surface) on both sides, with fair drape. Often used for nightwear.

Gabardine

Produced from a variety of fibres and similar to drill, gabardine may be light, medium or heavy weight. Comes in plain colours and is therefore suited to surface decoration.

Gingham

A plain-weave, inexpensive fabric, with yarn-dyed checks. Has good drape and is suited to colonial plays and interior settings such as kitchens.

Jersey

A single knit fabric with good drape, making it very suitable for Greek and Roman costumes. Fabrics made of natural fibres are the first choice for this purpose.

Linen

Produced in a variety of weights and used extensively for clothing, from the late nineteenth to the early twentieth century, especially for skirts and motoring coats. Expensive nowadays, so an alternative such as cotton may better suit the budget.

Organdie

A thin, translucent fabric made of cotton or synthetic yarns. Has a shiny finish, which makes it suitable for coats, waistcoats and jackets.

Poplin

Usually made of cotton but synthetic blends are also available. A crisp fabric that flows well, with a dull finish. Well suited to nineteenth-century women's skirts and suits, dresses, blouses and a variety of period clothing.

Sateen

A strong, lustrous, satin weave made of cotton. Although primarily used for lining, it can be used for garments that require a stiff, crisp appearance, such as dresses, blouses, breeches, coats and jackets.

Satin

This term refers to a basic weave and to fibres woven by this method. Varieties include: duchesse satin, a heavy, rich-looking satin; slipper satin, used among other things for evening slippers; and double-faced satin, which has a shiny appearance on both sides and is available in normal dress weight.

Serge

A hard-wearing twill, traditionally woven from wool. Nowadays it is often blended with synthetic fibres. Has poor drape, making it suitable for suits.

Shantung

A plain-weave, rough fabric, originally made of silk, with an interesting texture that looks good on stage.

Silk

Being an expensive fabric, silk is generally not suitable for school productions. Synthetic equivalents are available.

Pongee

Lightweight silk fabric with irregularities in the yarn.

Surah

A twill weave with a high sheen.

Thai silk

A heavyweight silk with a slub finish, made in Thailand.

Tussah

Made from wild, uncultivated silkworms. It is tan in colour, with a rougher texture than cultivated silk. Suitable for making peasant or beggar costumes, as it 'ages' very well.

Taffeta

Originally made of silk but now also made of rayon and acetate. A stiff, shiny fabric, which rustles when worn as a petticoat or skirt. Ideal for dresses, skirts, blouses and breeches.

Velveteen

A cotton pile fabric with a stiff drape. Can be used as a substitute for the more expensive velvet, with the exception of black velvet. (Velvet appears a richer black under stagelights.) Suitable for elaborate period costumes.

Theatrical sewing techniques

The following techniques are particularly useful to the costume designer.

Invisible stitch

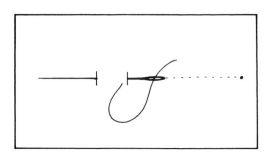

Used when an almost invisible line of stitching is required.

Slip stitch

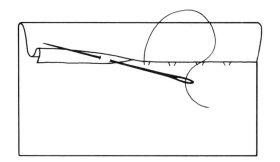

An almost invisible stitch used to sew hems and attach linings and pockets.

Hooks and eyes

A common costume closing that allows actors to get in and out of clothing quickly. They come in various sizes:

- Large sizes — Heavy skirts
- Medium sizes — Length of a bodice
- Small sizes — Collars and cuffs.

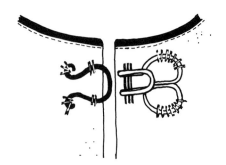

Hooks and eyes tapes

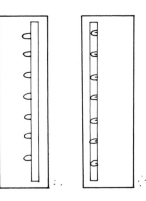

These save time, especially when used on a bodice.

Developing patterns

In the case of a complicated design, designers often have a *muslin* sample of the garment made first. This allows the designer to check the design before good-quality fabric is cut.

When you have finished with a pattern, don't throw it away. Store it in a manila envelope with information such as pattern size, style, historical period, name and date of production and a simple sketch. This will allow your school to build up a costume wardrobe. Your school may not do the same production again, but the pattern can be adapted for other productions.

Collect used commercial patterns, as they may form the basis of a costume for your next production.

The costume wardrobe

Never throw anything away. Nearly everything can be cut down or made into something else.

Loose skirts and trousers

These can be held up with safety pins, ribbon or drapery tape. Suitable for clowns', old people's and hobos' costumes.

Large trousers

These can be rolled up, gathered, pinned or held with a sash. Suitable for sailors', clowns', pirates' and dance costumes.

Fold the trousers over at the waist and secure with safety pins. A large sash can then be tied around the waist.

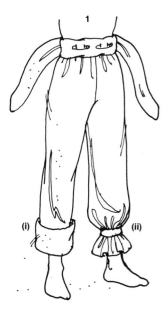

1

(i)   (ii)

Change the style and period of costume by altering the legs.
(i) fold up as cuffs
(ii) gather and tie —
with bands of fabric

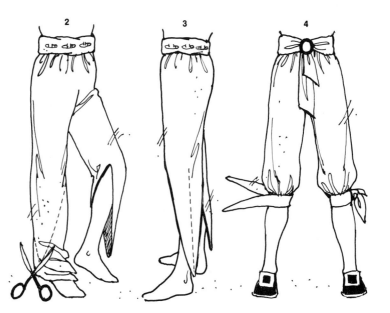

2, 3 & **4** show how the style can be altered by cutting diagonally up the trouser leg. Suitable for pirates.

Cut and gather old trousers to required length. Period costume such as Puritans.

2   3   4

Aprons and bustles

By changing or adding aprons, bustles and overskirts, you can change the character and period of a costume. How do the apron styles shown change the character of the costume?

Making a bustle

Fold a large piece of fabric in half and fill with wadding. Slip stitch the opening, and then drape with ribbons and bows.

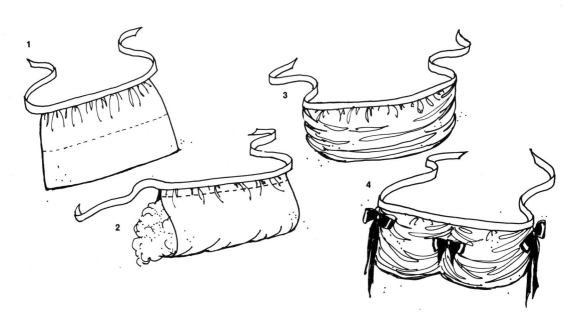

Collars and cuffs

An old garment can be altered with little cost to suit a particular period by adding collars and cuffs. Collect old lace, sheets and netting to make collars.

Elizabethan collars

Old lace can be cut to shape and backed with iron-on interfacing to help make the collar stand up and hold its shape. Fine wire can also be threaded through lace.

Peter Pan collars

These can be made from felt, stiff paper, white fabric and iron-on interfacing.

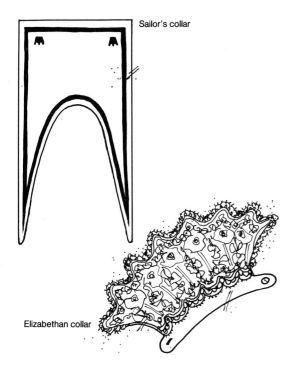

Sailor's collar

Elizabethan collar

Epaulettes

These are used on army and navy uniforms. Collect shoe boxes, ice-cream containers, heavy cardboard, string, cement glue, buttons and gold spray paint for making epaulettes.

(1) Cut the epaulette to size.

(2) Glue string (braid) onto the epaulette.
(3) Spray with gold paint.
(4) Attach the epaulette to the costume with button loops.

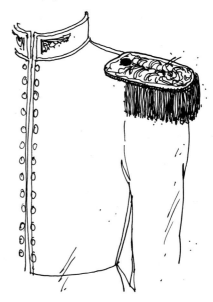

Activity

(1) As a class, collect the items listed above.
(2) Experiment with making epaulettes.
Note: Round ice-cream containers are the most useful here.

Ears, masks and tails

These can be made from fabric, cardboard, felt and stiff paper. They can be glued in place, but a few stitches and a button or two could save a few embarrassing moments!

Ears can be made from fabric, cardboard and felt — cut ears to size and shape required (use a button and button loop to attach the ears).

Use cardboard to form nose shapes. String and buttons can be used to prevent mask from falling off.

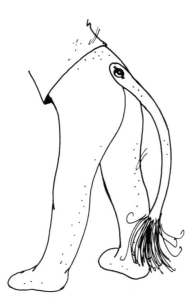

Tails can be buttoned or stitched into place. Fabric is suitable but other materials can be used.

Draping and folding

This method is suitable for plays set in Ancient Greek and Roman times. Costumes can be made from a sheet decorated with ribbons, bias tape or painting.

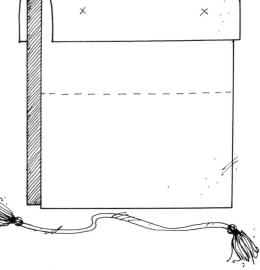

Fold over two sheets and tie around the waist to make an ancient costume.

The pagne

A garment worn by Africans and South Sea Islanders, the *pagne* should reach from the ground to the waist and wrap around the body about three times. To make your pagne authentic, use plain fabric and paint or draw an appropriate design.

Padding

Padding is used to make people appear bigger. A character may have a big stomach or chest or a shoulder hump, for example. There are two methods of padding.

Method 1

Sew a calico garment that fits the *torso*. Build up the required area by padding it with washable foam rubber or fibrefill. To hold the padding in place, cover it with a piece of stretch fabric and sew into place.

Method 2

This is a very simple method. You will need two T-shirts, one slightly bigger than the other. Put one T-shirt on, and place padding where it is needed. Put the second T-shirt over the top, and sew the two T-shirts together loosely to hold the padding in place.

This method is temporary, so it is suitable for only one or two performances.

Costume detail

Fabric dyes and paints

Dyes and paints can be used to give costumes character. They can 'age' costumes, make them look scruffy or simply add colour and are a useful method when money and time are limited.

Painting costumes

Use fabric dye paste or screen printing dyes. Heat set the paint when dry to prevent smudging. Small patterns and borders can be painted on after the garment is completed.

Activity

Using a piece of plain-coloured fabric 15 cm × 20 cm and screen-printing paste, design and paint a border for a Roman costume.

(1) What problems did you have?
(2) How could these problems be prevented in the future?

Shading costumes

Shading is used to help create a mood for a special scene. It can be achieved by applying colour to the fabric with a sponge.

Activity

Using a piece of plain-coloured fabric 15 cm × 20 cm, a sponge and leather dye, experiment with shading colour.

Note: Good shading should blend into the material with no definite starting or stopping point.

When deciding on the colour of a costume, you need to consider what type of stage lighting will be used. Lighting can change colours and therefore the effect you are trying to create.

Aging costumes

This technique gives a garment a comfortable, lived-in appearance or changes a garment's shape and proportion. There are several methods of aging costumes:

- Removing sharp creases from the garment
- Washing and drycleaning several times without ironing
- Rubbing elbows with wax to give a shiny appearance
- Using a grate to wear areas
- Sandpapering buttons
- Dusting with powder to give an old, dusty appearance.

Papier mâché

Papier mâché is used to make masks, noses, jewellery, armour and helmets. Lightweight and easily painted or decorated, it is a cheap method of making costumes.

To make *papier mâché*:

(1) Cut newspaper into long 3 cm wide strips.
(2) In a plastic bucket, make a heavy glue of flour and water.
(3) Soak the paper strips in paste for twenty minutes. They are then ready to shape.
(4) Allow to dry before decorating.

Note: Depending on the weather, drying could take several days.

Activities

(1) **Making a helmet or mask**

   (a) Obtain a polystyrene head of the kind used to store wigs.
   (b) Design a helmet or mask over the shape.
   (c) Allow to dry, paint, and remove.

Note: A balloon can be used to make helmets. Cover with *papier mâché* and shape when dry. Burst the balloon after the shape has set.

(2) **Making body armour**

   (a) Using cardboard boxes, cut a shape for your front and back. Tape to fit. Remove.
   (b) Tape the front and back pieces onto a board. Cover with *papier mâché*.
   (c) When dry, cut to the shape required. Undercoat with white paint and decorate to suit the character.

- Cut and shape paper/cardboard to fit.
- Tape cardboard into place.
- Remove by cutting down sides under the arms.
- You are now ready to apply the papier mâché. This method will make armour, helmets and shields.

Hats

Heavy cardboard can be used to make hats. They can then be decorated with paint, ribbon, braid and feathers. This method is particularly suitable for top hats and sun hats.

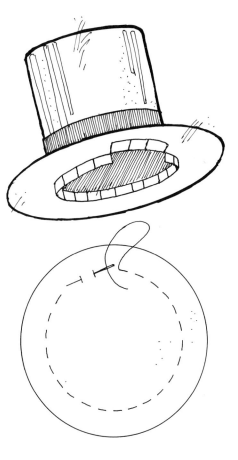

Mobcaps
Gather a large round piece of fabric, using hat elastic and small running stitches.

Skull cap and wig base
A stocking makes a good wig base. Material such as raw wool can then be glued on to make the required hairstyle.

Baldness
Use a skin-coloured swimming cap, cut to size.

Shoes

Gold and silver buckles added to lace-up shoes can make them into a period shoe. Buckles can be made from stiff cardboard and painted or covered.

Accessories

Jewellery and other clothing accessories must be in keeping with the play. Begin by collecting old jewellery from family and friends. Known as costume jewellery, it will add the final touch to your design.

Make-up

Make-up can be expensive. Here are some ideas to keep costs down:

- On stage, people need heavier make-up, as the lights tend to make them look washed out. Very white complexions are needed by clowns and ghosts. To achieve this effect, cover the face with vaseline, and then dust with talcum powder or cornflour.
- Eyebrow pencils are useful to draw facial and age lines, beards and moustaches. Remember, if you make a person's face older, you must do their hands too. Why is this?
- Old lipsticks, rouge and eyeshadow help to add variety.

— Eyeshadow under eyes makes people look older.
— When aging a person, follow the natural facial lines. Ask the person to smile, frown or look sad — these lines should be drawn in to make the person look the part.

Note: Make-up should never be harmful. Do not use anything that cannot be removed with soap and water.

Words to remember

accessories	muslin
durable	bodice
authentic	*pagne*
selvedge	torso

Activity 1 — Making a collage

You will need

- Fabric samples and trims
- Fabric glue
- Cardboard, pencils, thick tracing paper or butcher's paper

Method

(1) Choose a style from *either* one of the following periods in English history: ● Plantagenet ● Tudor ● Elizabethan *or* an Asian or African culture.
(2) Place tracing paper over the figure selected and carefully outline the silhouette and detail.
(3) Research the fabrics used for the garment. Although the exact fabric may not be available, try to obtain a similar one. Cut the fabric to size and glue on the figure silhouette.
(4) Trim as necessary.
(5) Write a one-page account of the costume of the English period or Asian or African culture chosen.

Activity 2

You have been asked to design costumes for a school play written by the drama class. The school has no costume department, and the budget is limited to £20.

The play takes place on a pirate ship during the sixteenth century. The captain and crew are an unruly group, with little time for fashion fineries. For the last twenty years, old Captain Grimes has sailed the seven seas with a crew of ten.

(1) Design suitable costumes for the captain and crew, using the figure outlines in Chapter 7 (p. 84).
(2) Make a list of suitable fabrics, colours and accessories.
(3) Make suggestions as to the type of make-up that would be suitable.

Activity 3

Your friend is to play the wife of a Puritan during the time Oliver Cromwell ruled England in her school play and has to provide her own costume. She has asked you for help.

(1) Design her costume.
(2) Suggest a suitable fabric, bearing in mind that she can spend up to £8 on the costume.
(3) Research the influence Cromwell had on costume, and write a one-page report.

Activity 4

The chorus for the school musical must wear Japanese costumes in the second act.

(1) Design the costume.
(2) Write a brief description of the costume.

Extension activity 1

In the year 2050 an interplanetary spaceship is to set off from Earth with twenty delegates to a conference of the Intergalactic Sports and Recreation Association, to be held on the planet Zinit. Design the costume to be worn by the delegates (who include both men and women).

Note: Because of the distance to be travelled, the costume must be made of a fabric that will adapt to atmospheric changes. This is es-

Opposite: When designing costume, take into account the culture, era and personality of the character.

pecially a problem on Zinit, where quite drastic weather changes occur with little warning.

Extension activity 2

Your school musical is set in the 1920s. There will be three principal actors, two female and one male.

(1) Design suitable day wear for each person.
(2) Indicate fabrics and colours. Explain the effect the lighting in the school hall will have on the colours you have selected for the costumes.

Glossary

Muslin — An unbleached, light cotton fabric.
Authentic — Genuine; resembling the original.
Torso — Trunk of the human body.

Further reading

Haley, G. *Costumes for Plays and Playing,* Methuen, London, 1977

10

Interior design

The *interior* decoration of a house or room reflects the *personality* of the people who live there.

When designing an interior, begin by deciding the room's main function. Often rooms have more than one function. For example, a bedroom may also be a study.

A decorator must think about style. A house is most comfortable when the same style is used throughout. Basically, a style may be *his-*

The stage of the life cycle a family is in will affect their furnishing needs.

toric with *antique* furniture or *contemporary* with *modern* furniture. Some people are able to mix both styles together with success.

Life cycle is a term used to describe the stages of life people go through. At each stage they will have different needs, and the way a house is decorated usually reflects this.

There are three stages in the life cycle of a family:

- *Establishing* — People marry and set up a home.
- *Expanding* — With the arrival of children, the family grows.
- *Contracting* — Grown-up children marry, leaving parents in the family home.

Activity

Divide the class into three groups. Each group is to select one stage of the family life cycle.

(1) Design or select a floor plan to suit the stage you have chosen.
(2) Collect pictures to illustrate suitable furnishings.

Principles of design

There are three important design principles, which will affect how good or bad an interior will be:

- Balance
- Rhythm
- Emphasis.

Symmetrical balance. Where is the line showing the axis of symmetry in this picture?

Balance

Another name for balance is 'visual weight'. Furniture, decoration and colour need to complement each other.

Balance can be *symmetrical* or *asymmetrical*. With symmetrical balance, both sides are exactly the same. Asymmetrical balance is uneven and can suggest movement.

Rhythm

Rhythm suggests movement. It can be achieved by *repetition*, which repeats angles, curves, colours or textures, or *progression*, which indicates an increase in size, shape or direction.

Emphasis

Attention needs to be given to one aspect of a room. If this is not done, a room may appear messy and have no *focal point*, such as a fireplace.

Other design principles

- *Harmony* — All parts combine; nothing appears to be out of place.
- *Proportion* — When all aspects of interior design combine satisfactorily, the size of each piece will be related to its importance.
- *Scale* — The size of an object in relation to other objects. The size of the various objects in a room should be consistent, so that they are in harmony with each other.

Space and *form* are two aspects of design that influence each other. Space in a room can be divided by furniture. Form gives shape to space.

Line outlines form or space in a room. There are two aspects to line: *size* and *direction*. The size of a line refers to its length. For example, a very wide, low couch with long, horizontal lines will make a room appear longer than it really is. Lines may go in any direction — vertical, horizontal or diagonal. The direction of the line will affect the feelings people have. For

The fireplace forms a *focal point* for the room.

example, horizontal lines are said to be peaceful and relaxing.

The texture of a fabric is a surface quality. Texture is both decorative and can be aesthetically pleasing.

Activity

Collect ten samples of textiles suitable for interior decoration, and paste them into your workbook. Explain how each might be used.

Light and colour

Light and colour are two aspects of the same quality. You cannot have one without the other.

Activity

Put a prism on a piece of white paper.

(1) What do you see on the white paper?
(2) What is natural (white) light made up of?

The colour of an object is the result of the way it reflects light.

Light is used to add interest. By using spotlights or lamps, dramatic effects can be obtained with bright and dark areas. Bright light is stimulating, while light from lamps is cool and restful.

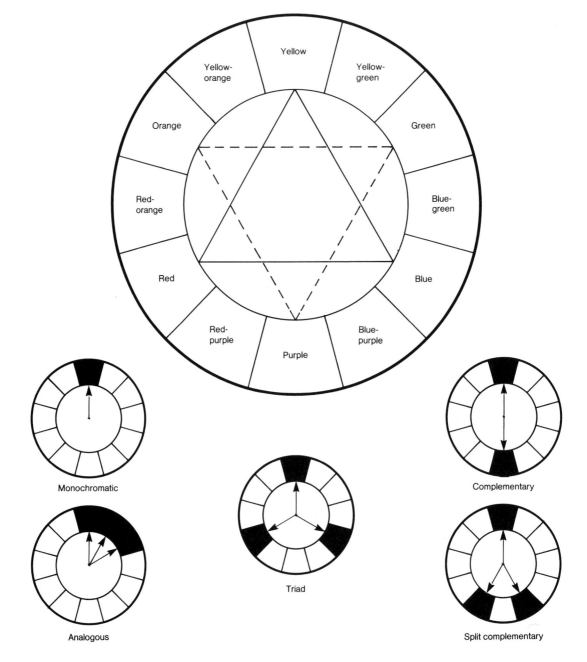

The colour wheel. Copy the wheel into your workbook and colour it in.

Colour has three major characteristics:

- *Hue* — Also known as the colour on the colour wheel.
- *Value* — Indicates how light or dark the colour is.
- *Intensity* — Used to indicate how much of the dominant hue (colour) is present in a colour made by mixing different colours.

When talking about *hue* (colour) on the colour wheel, two terms are used: *analogous*, which means that the colours are next to each other on the colour wheel, for example yellow and yellow-green, and *complementary*, where colours lie directly opposite each other on the colour wheel, for example red and green.

Activity

You will need

- Small paint brush
- Tubes of water paint — red, blue, yellow
- Sheets of white paper

Method

(1) Draw a circle, and divide it into twelve equal parts.
(2) Using a colour wheel as a guide, mix your paints to get the same hues. Paint in the colours.
(3) When dry, cut the colour wheel out and paste it into your workbook. Underneath your colour wheel, answer these questions:
  (a) Which colours are bright, warm or active?
  These are referred to as *advancing* hues.
  (b) Which colours are cool, restful and calm?
  Such colours are known as *receding* hues.

Colour schemes

When choosing a colour scheme for a home, the following factors need to be considered:

- Stage of the life cycle — For example, older people may prefer quieter colours.

- Possessions — Consider what people already have; careful selection of colour could bring everything together.
- The room — Walls and windows are the main areas to be coloured; consider the amount of light in a room as well as its size.

When choosing colours for a room, there are different colour schemes to choose from. A *monochromatic* scheme uses one hue (colour), with variations from light to dark. An *analogous* scheme has three or more hues, which should be harmonious. A *complementary* scheme uses two hues that are opposite each other on the colour wheel. There is a fourth scheme known as a *triad*, which is made up of any three colours of equal distance from the other on the colour wheel.

Decorating with textiles

Floors

The choice of floor coverings will depend on the use of the room. Kitchens need easy-care surfaces, because they are in constant use. Vinyl and cork tiles are two examples of suitable materials. They are also suitable for use in bathrooms, though carpet and carpet tiles with a rubberised backing are now often used for a warmer and softer surface. Generally, other rooms are carpeted.

Carpets

There are many varieties of carpets to choose from, and carpets are produced in a variety of ways.

Wilton carpet is produced on a Jacquard loom. Patterns are produced by the use of coloured yarns. When a coloured yarn is not required, it is carried along the back of the carpet, which makes Wilton a long-wearing carpet.

Axminster carpets have the greatest colour range. The *pile* is usually cut to one length. To identify an Axminster carpet, look on the back, where heavy ridges can be seen.

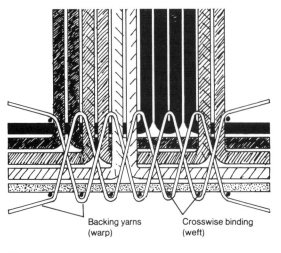

Backing yarns (warp)   Crosswise binding (weft)

Wilton

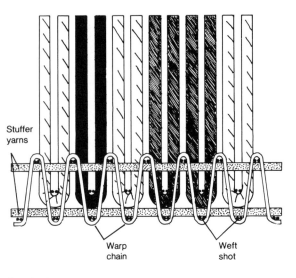

Stuffer yarns

Warp chain   Weft shot

Axminster

The fibres used to make the yarn determine how well a carpet will wear. A carpet that has the following properties is a good choice:

- Resilience
- Elasticity
- Warmth
- Easy to clean
- Durability (resistance to wear)
- Resistance to insects
- Absorbs sound
- Resistance to static electricity
- Inflammability

Activity

Collect offcuts of different carpets, and carefully pull them apart.

(1) How were the loops formed?
(2) Describe the back of the carpet.
(3) Compare the construction of each carpet.

A floor covering that is very expensive and highly prized is the *oriental rug*. True oriental rugs are hand-knotted onto a woven backing and are made in China, India, Iran and Turkey. They are expensive because of the intricate design, the time required to make them

and the closeness of the pile. The closer the pile, the more durable the rug.

The first step in making an oriental rug is to knot a row of pile yarns. Two rows of weft yarns are then woven across the rug. Both pile and weft yarns are packed down tightly onto the other yarns. This process is then repeated until the rug is the required size. The main fibre used in the yarn is wool, but silk, cotton, linen and camel hair may also be used.

The rug takes the name of the place where it was produced. For example, Persian rugs are made in Iran (formerly Persia) and feature flowers, leaves and birds.

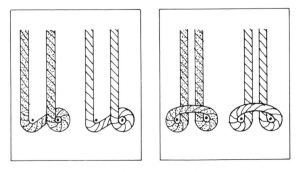

Knots for Oriental Rugs may be made in one of two ways. A Persian (or *Sehna*) knot, left, twists the pile and warp yarns together. A Turkish (or *Ghiordes*) knot, right, ties them together.

An Oriental rug from Turkey

A Chinese carpet

Man-made or natural fibre?

Rugs and carpets containing man-made fibres absorb moisture slowly, are *non-allergenic* and are not affected by moths and mildew. They do, however, build up static electricity. Natural fibres are not affected by static electricity but require more care to prevent moths and mildew becoming a problem.

Choosing rugs and carpets

- The colour chosen must blend with other aspects of the room. Remember that medium colours and patterns do not show dirt as easily as very light or dark colours and plain carpets.
- By varying the carpet surface, interest can be added to a room.
- Carpet helps to insulate a room and so saves energy.

Activity

Visit a department store that sells a variety of floor coverings. Collect pamphlets, and paste them in your workbook as a reference for future design work.

Curtains and furnishings

Fabrics for curtains and furniture can be costly. Before buying fabrics, analyse the room and your needs carefully.

If a room faces the west, it will get the afternoon sun, which will fade curtains. Therefore, choose colours that won't fade, or provide extra protection such as blinds. Lined curtains insulate a room more effectively than unlined curtains.

Curtains are an aid to controlling privacy, temperature and light, and all these aspects need to be considered when decorating a room.

Interior decorating fabric chart

Because each fibre has different properties, you need to decide what you expect from a fabric before you make your choice. See p. 136.

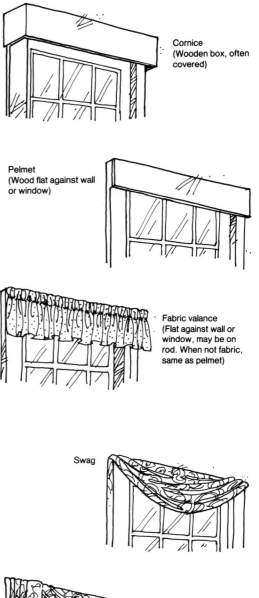

Cornice
(Wooden box, often covered)

Pelmet
(Wood flat against wall or window)

Fabric valance
(Flat against wall or window, may be on rod. When not fabric, same as pelmet)

Swag

Swag and tails

Fibre	Performance	Care and uses
Acetate	Weakened by sunlight.	Dryclean. Curtains and some upholstery
Acrylic	Will pill. Resistant to sunlight.	Warm wash. Curtains and some upholstery
Cotton	Colour may be affected by sunlight. Unless treated will crease easily.	Washes well but can also be drycleaned, depending on construction. All decorative uses
Glass	May crack. Can cause skin irritation.	Curtains
Linen	Durable, but creases unless treated.	Dryclean or wash. All decorative uses
Mod acrylic	Sensitive to heat.	Pile fabrics to be drycleaned. Rugs, upholstery and pile fabrics
Nylon	Pale colours fade.	Machine wash curtains. Upholstery and rugs
Polyesters	May pill or attract lint.	Machine wash. All decorative uses
Rayon	Generally a weak fibre. Affected by sunlight.	Dryclean. All decorative uses
Silk	Weakened by sunlight.	Dryclean. Expensive to use for decoration.
Wool	Unless treated, will shrink and attract moths.	Dryclean. All decorative uses

Fibre care chart

Care of fabrics

To maintain the good appearance of your textiles, wipe up spills quickly before they become a permanent stain.

Some spills wipe off or can be removed with water. If a stain needs further treatment, try the treatment first on an area that will not be seen. Sometimes stain removal damages fibres or removes the colour.

Fabric finishes

To make fabric more durable, a number of special finishes have been developed.

Anti-static

Static electricity is a problem with acetates, nylons and polyesters, as these fabrics are not very absorbent. It also causes soil to remain on the fabric.

Stain	Solvent or reagent
Chewing gum	Rub with ice cube to harden gum, then scrape off excess. Use drycleaning solvent with care, as it could spread the stain.
Grass	Methylated spirits
Nail polish	Nail polish remover (care needed, as this can seriously damage some fabrics). Never use on acetate or triacetate.
Ball-point pen	Sponge with methylated spirit, rinse well and launder thoroughly. A specially formulated stain remover can be bought. Follow the directions with the product.
Tea and coffee	Wash as soon as possible.

Stain removal

Anti-static finishes work by improving the ability of the fabric surface to conduct electricity or by attracting molecules of water to the fabric surface. Some fabrics have chemical finishes that neutralise the electrostatic charges. Fabric softeners added to the wash also help to do this.

Activity

(1) Obtain five fabric samples of acetate, nylon, polyester, cotton and wool.
(2) Rub one at a time along a glass rod or plastic comb.
(3) Using a glass rod or plastic comb, try to pick up small pieces of paper.

   (a) Which fabrics caused the rod or comb to attract the paper?
   These fabrics have become *electrostatically* charged.
   (b) What problems would be caused by household fabrics building up static electricity?

Anti-bacterial

An antiseptic finish can be applied, usually in the final finishing process, which will inhibit bacterial growth. It stops the development of perspiration and other odours. It is often used for socks, baby's plastic pants and shoes. The finish is not affected by washing or dry cleaning.

Mothproofing

Wool contains a protein known as *keratin*, and because of this it attracts moths and carpet beetles.

Naphthalene gives off a smell that repels moths and prevents them from depositing eggs on the fabric. It can be readily bought in a chemist's.

Manufacturers can apply an insecticide to the fabric, but this may not be permanent. Another finish has been developed that changes the protein structure in the fibre, and this is said to be permanent.

Keeping carpets clean helps to prevent damage from moths and beetles.

Water-repellent and waterproof

Both water-repellent and waterproof finishes coat the fabric to stop water passing through. Water-repellent fabrics are more suitable for most domestic purposes, as they allow some air to pass through.

Scotchgard is the name of a fluorochemical finish which can be bought in aerosol cans and applied in the home. It resists water and stains and is suitable for such things as fabric chairs.

Stain- and soil-resistant

These finishes can create an electric charge that resists soil or produce a smooth surface that soil will not adhere to.

Heat-reflectant

These finishes are used to improve insulation. Heat-reflectant finishes may be sprayed onto closely woven fabric.

When buying fabrics with special finishes, ask yourself these questions:

- Will the finish meet my need?
- Does it need special cleaning?
- Will the finish wash off?

Activity — Consumer survey

(1) Divide the class into five groups to investigate finishes given to household textiles.
(2) Each group is to select one of the following articles:
   Household linen
      Blankets
      Towels
      Sheets or duvet covers
      Pillowcases
      Tablecloths
   Curtains and curtain fabrics
   Floor coverings — carpets and rugs
   Mattresses and pillows
   Fabric-covered furniture.
(3) Visit shops and list the finishes given to the type of article you are investigating.
(4) Report your findings to the class. Which articles have the most finishing processes? Why is this?

Embroidery

For many hundreds of years people have added decoration to their homes by embroidery. Some countries have developed embroidery methods that have been done by generation after generation. Some examples of these include *Spanish blackwork* from Spain, *tapestry* from England, *hardanger* from Norway and *couching* from China.

Nowadays people still do traditional embroideries, but more people are starting to try *creative embroidery*. This involves creating different designs by combining a variety of stitches and techniques developed over the years.

Activity

(1) Design a pattern you would like to embroider. Nature provides interesting designs — look at shells, stones and cane baskets, all of which have interesting textures to embroider.

You can make a 'pattern' by placing paper over the item and rubbing it with a 4B pencil.

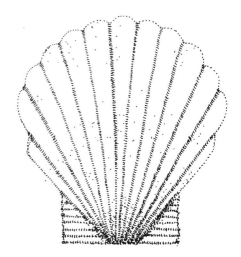

A shell rubbing

Fruit and vegetables are another source of ideas. Cut a capsicum, apple or pear in half. Draw what you see.

Looking down on a flower head

Back stitch

Threaded back stitch

Herringbone stitch

Whipped back stitch

Loop stitch

Bullion knot

Chain stitch

Couching

Fly stitch

Fishbone stitch

French knot

Satin stitch

Sheaf filling stitch

Stem stitch

Straight stitch

Detached chain stitch

Loop stitch

Crewel embroidery stitches. Use these stitches to outline your rubbing activity.

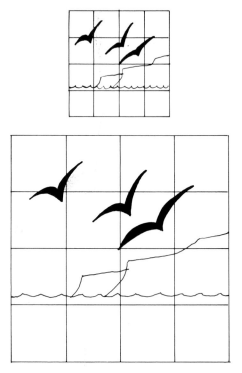

1. Divide the chosen design into squares.
2. Draw an outline of the size required, and divide this area into the same number of squares.
3. Copy the design square by square.

Sometimes a design needs to be enlarged. First divide the design into squares (overlaying a sheet of transparent paper if necessary). Next, on a sheet of paper, outline the size required and divide this area into the same number of squares. Then copy the design square by square onto your paper.

(2) Decide on the stitches to be used.
(3) Transfer your pattern onto plain furnishing fabric, using dressmaker's carbon.
(4) Embroider and complete as required.

Words to remember

interior	repetition
personality	harmony
historic	proportion
antique	scale

contemporary	texture
modern	aesthetic
establishing	hue
expanding	value
contracting	intensity
balance	analogous
symmetrical	complementary
asymmetrical	fluorochemical
rhythm	

Revision exercises

(1) How does life cycle affect the decoration of a home?
(2) Explain the difference between symmetrical and asymmetrical balance. Draw a sketch to illustrate the difference.
(3) How is the mood of a room affected by colour?
(4) When decorators use the following terms, what are they referring to?
  (a) Hue
  (b) Analogous
  (c) Oriental rugs
  (d) Monochromatic
(5) What can the consumer use to protect wool fabrics?
(6) (a) Unscramble the letters to find terms that have been discussed in this chapter.

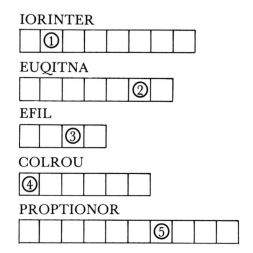

IORINTER

EUQITNA

EFIL

COLROU

PROPTIONOR

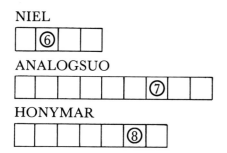

NIEL

ANALOGSUO

HONYMAR

(b) Draw the letters from the circles in the squares:

1 2 3 4 5 6 7 8

(c) Unscramble the letters to complete this sentence:

Design should suit the ------- of a room.

Extension activity 1

As an interior decorator, you have been asked to decorate a bedroom for a six-year-old girl *or* boy. The bedroom faces west.

(1) Compile a folder with the following information. Make use of photographs, samples and colour charts.
- Furniture
- Furnishing fabrics
- Colour schemes
- Explanation of your choices
(2) Present your portfolio to the class for discussion.

Extension activity 2

(1) Select a country you are interested in, and investigate the dominant style of interior design.
(2) Write up your results, using illustrations where necessary.
(3) Report your findings to the class.

Extension activity 3

Design a bedroom for a sixteen-year-old girl *or* boy. The bedroom is 4 m × 4 m and faces east.

Prepare a folder as in Extension Activity 1.

Glossary

Antique — Belonging to a past time.
Contemporary — Belonging to the same time; modern.
Aesthetic — Concerned with an appreciation of what is beautiful.
Resilient — A property of a fabric which allows it to return to its original shape after stretching.
Elasticity — The ability to stretch.

Further reading

The Laura Ashley Book of Home Decorating, Octopus, 1982
Terence Conran's New House Book, Octopus Conran, 1985
Gilliatt, M. *The Complete Book of Home Design*, Orbis, 1984

11

Man-made fibres

The first man-made fibres were produced in 1883 by Robert Swan. These fibres were used as filaments in electric light bulbs. In the past 100 years, many types of man-made fibres have been produced for particular needs, and many more will be made in the future.

There are two types of man-made fibres: *regenerated* and *synthetic*.

Regenerated fibres are made from plant materials such as wood. The cellulose in wood is treated to produce fibres such as viscose rayon, acetate and triacetate.

Synthetic fibres are made from raw materials such as coal or oil. The first synthetic fibre, produced in 1935, was nylon. Later, polyesters and acrylics were developed.

Producing man-made fibres

(1) Materials used to make the fibres are converted into a liquid form.
(2) The liquid is forced through tiny holes in a spinneret. As the fibres are forced through the spinneret, they harden.

Fibres extruded through a spinneret.

(3) There are three methods of hardening the fibres:
(a) *Dry spinning*
The fibres are extruded into a hot chamber. The acetone in the fibres evaporates as a result of the heat intensity, forming solid fibres.

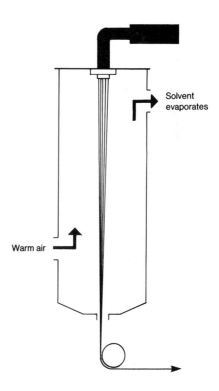

Solvent evaporates

Warm air

In dry spinning, solid fibres are produced as they dry in a heated chamber.

(b) *Wet spinning*

Fibres are forced from the spinneret into a bath containing an acid that hardens the fibres. This method is used in the production of viscose rayon.

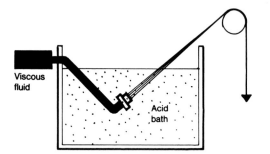

(c) *Melt spinning*

Solid pieces of fibre are melted, forced through a spinneret and then solidified again in a stream of cold air.

This method is used in the production of nylon and polyesters such as Dacron and Terylene.

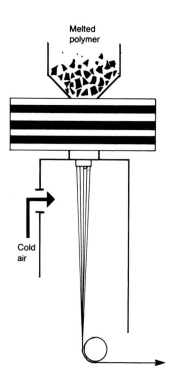

(4) Next fibres are stretched. This is known as *drawing* and makes the fibres stronger for spinning.

(5) If a multifilament yarn is desired, filaments from the spinneret are twisted together.

If a staple spun yarn is desired, filaments are cut into short lengths and then spun to form yarn.

Activity

(1) *Making nylon (or 'the nylon rope trick')*

You will need

- 0.9 g 1.6 diaminohexane
- 0.4 ml sebacyl chloride or adipyl chloride
- 20 ml carbon tetrachloride
- 2 small beakers
- Forceps
- Empty cotton reel

Method

(1) Dissolve the 1.6 diaminohexane in 10 ml of water in a beaker.
(2) Dissolve the sebacyl chloride in the carbon tetrachloride in another beaker.
(3) *Carefully* pour the 1.6 diaminohexane solution down the inner sides of the second beaker, so that it forms a layer on top of the carbon tetrachloride solution.
(4) The solution will not mix, but a skin will form at the boundary between them.
(5) Slowly lift the skin out with the forceps, and wind the skin around a cotton reel.

(2) *Making an acetate filament*

You will need

- 50 ml acetone
- 5 g acetate fibres or fabric
- Beaker
- Shallow plate
- Stirring rod

Method

(1) Place the acetone in a beaker with the acetate fibres or fabric.
(2) Pour the solution into a shallow dish, and place it in the sun to evaporate.

(3) Once the acetone has evaporated, a thin filament of acetate can be drawn from the plate, using the head of a pin.

Properties of man-made fibres

Thermoplasticity

Only acetate and synthetic fibres are *thermoplastic*. The word thermoplastic means 'able to be moulded by heat'. (*Thermo* means heat, and *plastic* means able to be moulded into various shapes.) This property makes possible the permanent heat setting of pleats, shaping pantyhose and crease resistant finishes.

Activity

Take two fabric samples, one cotton and one nylon. Using a moderately hot iron, try to pleat each sample.

Answer the following questions:

(1) Which fabric gave the best results?
(2) Which fabric retains the pleats when crushed?

Water absorption

Many synthetics, such as nylon and polyester, are *hydrophobic*. This means that they do not absorb moisture easily. This property makes synthetics uncomfortable to wear in hot, humid climates. Synthetic underwear does not absorb perspiration, so cotton, wool and silk are better fabrics for this purpose.

Activity

Drop water from an eye dropper onto a piece of cotton fabric and a piece of nylon fabric. Record the time it takes for the water to be absorbed into the fabric.

Answer the following questions:

(1) Which fabric was the most water absorbent?
(2) Which fabric was the most water repellent?

(3) What factors may decrease the ability of some fabrics to absorb water on their surface?

Imitation of natural fibres

Acrylics, particularly Orlon, are used to substitute for or imitate wool. The filaments are cut into staple lengths and crimped to appear like wool. The crimping produces bulkiness, which gives warmth. It is often difficult to identify the differences between an Orlon jumper and a woollen jumper. Although acrylics have some elasticity, they are not resilient like wool and therefore pull out of shape easily. One big advantage of acrylics is that they wash easily and are resistant to sunlight.

Activity

You will need

- Two samples of white or cream knitted fabric, one wool and one Orlon. Cut each into two, approximately 4 cm × 4 cm, and keep one piece of each as a control.

Method

(1) Place a sample of wool and a sample of Orlon in sunlight for five hours.
(2) Wash each sample vigorously for ten minutes in hot soapy water.
(3) Rinse in cold water. Allow to dry.
(4) Place a drop of water on each sample and compare the time it takes for it to be absorbed.
(5) Compare the two samples, noting changes in colour, size and fibre structure.
(6) Do the thermoplasticity test described in the previous column for each sample.

Results

Record your results in a table like the following:

Wool	Orlon

	Cotton		Nylon	
	With Scotchguard	Without Scotchguard	With Scotchguard	Without Scotchguard
Water repellency				
Soil resistance				

Pilling

Pilling can be seen on many garments as small balls of fibres clinging to the surface. Pills break off easily from natural fibre garments, but they do not come off synthetics and can make the garment look unsightly, especially where a large amount of rubbing has occurred. Pilling can be prevented by twisting yarns tightly in the manufacturing process.

Anti-static treatment

Because synthetic garments are not very absorbent, static electricity builds up in them, causing them to cling to the wearer. It can even give a slight electric shock. Some fabrics are treated with chemicals to neutralise the electrostatic charge. This is known as an anti-stat finish.

Synthetics can be temporarily treated to reduce static electricity by adding a fabric softener to the final rinse when washing.

Water repellency

Most synthetics repel water from their surface because they are *hydrophobic* fibres. This quality makes synthetics, such as nylon and polyester, particularly suitable for such things as boat sails, ski-wear, raincoats and tents. In addition, their lightweight construction makes synthetics easy to carry and fold.

Fabrics such as cotton that are not naturally waterproof can be coated with a hydrophobic chemical, which reacts with the fibres to provide a finish that is both waterproof and soil resistant. A product called Scotchguard can be applied to make fabrics water repellent.

Activity

(1) Spray Scotchguard on two pieces of fabric, one nylon and one cotton.
(2) Place a drop of water on each piece of fabric. Observe what happens after ten minutes.
(3) Rub each piece of fabric with a drop of oil.
(4) Draw up a table like the one above in your workbook to show the results.
    (a) Which fabric is more water repellent?
    (b) Which fabric is more soil resistant?

Recently developed synthetic fibres

Elastomeric fibres

An elastomeric fibre will stretch to about five times its length and will snap back again to its original size. *Lycra* is the trade name of a fabric made from elastomeric fibre. It is used for swimwear, exercise clothes and underwear. Its elasticity makes it comfortable to wear, as it stretches with body movement.

Elastomeric fibres are also used for bandages, knee and elbow supports and hosiery. They can be used in any combination with natural or synthetic fibres.

Polyvinyl chloride (P.V.C.) fibres

Most people call polyvinyl either P.V.C. or vinyl. Because it is like a plastic, it is uncomfortable to wear in humid conditions or next to the skin. The most common uses include 'fake leather' jackets, shoes, bags, upholstery in cars and lounges, kitchen flooring and paint.

Glass fibres

Molten glass is extruded through a spinneret to form a monofilament fibre. It is mainly used for fibreglass boats, surfboards, flameproof curtains and protective overalls.

Metallic fibres

Lurex and lamé are shiny fibres made from aluminium and coated with polyester to protect the surface. These fibres can be used for decorative stitching threads, fabrics for theatrical and evening wear and handbags.

Words to remember

regenerated	pilling
wet spinning	elastomeric
dry spinning	Lycra
melt spinning	repellent
spinneret	Scotchguard
multifilament yarn	lurex
synthetic	lamé
staple spun yarn	polyvinyl chloride
thermoplastic	polyamide
thermoplasticity	Orlon
hydrophobic	acrylic
absorb	Terylene

Revision exercise 1

Fill in the missing words to complete the sentences:

(1) A group of fibres developed recently that have the ability to stretch and recover are ----------- fibres. (11 letters)

(2) Another name for Terylene is ------. (6 letters)

(3) A lightweight acrylic used as a substitute for wool is -----. (5 letters)

(4) A ------------ is a long, never-ending fibre. (12 letters)

(5) The process that produces nylon is called ---- --------. (4 letters) (8 letters)

(6) Nylon belongs to a group of fibres called ---------. (9 letters)

(7) Molten nylon is passed through a --------- to produce monofilament fibres. (9 letters)

(8) ----------- fibres are made from cellulosic material such as wood. (11 letters)

(9) Most metallic yarns are made from ---------. (9 letters)

(10) The other name for plastic or P.V.C. is --------- --------. (9 letters) (8 letters)

Revision exercise 2

Unscramble the following words to find the names of man-made fibres:

RYLAC	TEATCAE
CVSSOIE	YAORN
OLONR	NLRODA
ONYLN	
ACDNOR	
PINEMCERL	
NEYTEREL	

Glossary

Polymer — A giant molecule made of many small units of atoms.
Solidify — To change from a liquid to a solid.
Solvent — A liquid with the power of dissolving a solid.
Viscous — Sticky, of a consistency like honey, just pourable.

12

Interesting fibres and fabrics

Protein fibres

Other animal fibres besides wool and silk can be used for yarn.

Alpaca

The alpaca is a native animal of South America. It is a species of llama and produces colourful fleeces, which are shorn once every two years. Colours include brown, grey, beige, fawn and a popular reddish brown. These colours are often seen in Peruvian jumpers and embroideries.

Angora

The Angora rabbit has very long, soft hair. The fibres are used for fabric blends and knitting wools.

Camel

Camel hair is collected as it falls off the animal; it is never shorn or cut. For this reason, camel hair fabrics are very expensive. The most common uses include rugs and coats.

Cashmere

The Kashmir goat, which lives in the Himalayas, has a very silky undercoat called cashmere. It is very expensive and used mainly for knitwear.

Llama

The llama, like the alpaca, is a native animal of South America. Its fleece is often blended with wool to produce a lightweight yet warm yarn.

Mohair

Mohair is the fleece of the Angora goat. It is a long, white fibre and is used mainly for knitwear, rugs and upholstery. The older the goat, the coarser the fibre; so the fleece from a kid goat, being much softer, is more valuable.

Horsehair

Horsehair was once commonly used for stuffing upholstered chairs and bedheads and was obtained by brushing horses. Today it has been replaced by P.V.C. foam, which is cheaper, softer and more easily obtained. Horsehair was also used for padding bustles in the early part of the twentieth century and shoulders in the seventeenth century.

Cellulosic fibres

Coir

The coarse hair of the coconut. Used for floor and doormats.

Kapok

The soft fibres from inside the seed pod of the Kapok (or ceiba) tree. Used mainly for stuffing, pillows, mattresses, sleeping bags and life jackets. After considerable wear, kapok is eventually reduced to powder, because of its brittle nature. Today, most pillows, quilts and sleeping bags are filled with synthetic polyester fibres, which are cheaper than kapok and do not break up.

Padded shoulders

Padded bustles, worn to emphasise the hour-glass shape — fashionable for women in the nineteenth and early twentieth centuries

Padded farthingale or skirt hoop to give an illusion of a small waist, worn in Elizabethan times (sixteenth century)

Horse hair was used to make bustles, and farthingales provided shape to the dress.

Hemp

Comes from the stems of the hemp plant. Because of its strength, it is used to make mooring rope for boats, canvas and tarpaulins.

Jute

Comes from the stems of jute plants. Like hemp, it is strong and inexpensive. It can be used for rope, twine, hessian bags and backing for carpet and linoleum. Because it is easily dyed, it is used for *macrame* work (see next page).

Sisal

A harsh, strong fibre, produced from the leaves of a certain type of plant. Sisal is rarely woven and is used to make twine, string and rope.

Macrame

Knotting probably developed in prehistoric times when two lengths of cord needed to be joined for some purpose. Once the beauty of knots, as well as their usefulness, was recognised, the new art form of *macrame* (pronounced mack-**ra**-may) emerged.

The Egyptians used to make fishnets and decorative fringes. Some of these objects still exist and can be seen in museums. Sailors developed the craft further and have carried it to many parts of the world. Today, macrame is practised as a leisure time activity, to produce such things as wall hangings, plant holders, jewellery and belts.

By using various types of yarns and adding beads and other ornaments, you can express your creativity in endless variations with a few basic knots.

Before starting to make something, take some thick cotton cord or jute string and practise the following *basic knots*.

Square knot

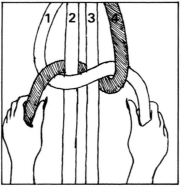

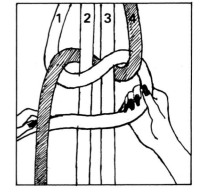

When tying a square knot, the two outside cords, **1** and **4**, are called **working cords** and the two inside cords, **2** and **3**, are called **holding cords**. Place cord **1** over cords **2** and **3** in an 'L' shape. Place cord **4** over the top of cord **1** at the end of the 'L'.

Now bring cord **4** under cords **2** and **3**. Pull cord **4** up through the hole between cords **1** and **2**.

To finish the square knot, bring cord **1** back over cords **3** and **2**. Place cord **4** over the top of cord **1**.

Alternating square knot

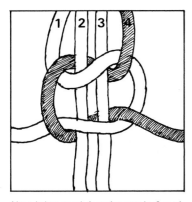

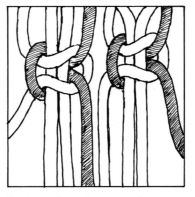

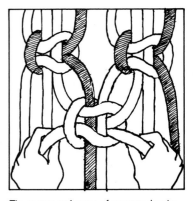

Now bring cord **4** under cords **2** and **3**. Pull cord **4** up through the hole between cords **3** and **1**. Pull your working cords up tightly against the first half of the knot. You will now have a complete square knot.

To tie an alternating square knot pattern, use eight cords and tie one square knot with each group of four cords, one knot alongside the other knot.

Tie a second row of square knots, using four cords — **3** and **4** from the square knot on the left and **1** and **2** from the square knot on the right. Tie one square knot using **4** and **1** for **holding** cords and **3** and **2** as **working** cords. This square knot should now join the first row together.

Wrap knot

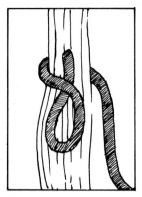  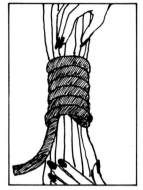

A wrap knot is done by bringing a group of cords together and placing the cord used for wrapping over the top of the cords, forming a loop.

Using the same cord you made the loop with, begin wrapping neatly around and around your group of cords, covering the loop completely under the wrapping.

When you have wrapped as much as you want, pull the end of the cord through the loop at the bottom of the wrap.

Pull the cord at the top, which will pull the loop and cord up and underneath the wrap. The loop should be completely hidden under the wrap. Trim off the top and bottom cord as close to the wrap as you can.

With a little practice, you will be able to keep an even tension or tightness.

Some yarns are easier to knot than others. Tightly twisted yarns, such as upholstery twine, parachute cord, and linen or cotton cord, are best for close, even knotting.

Sisal, jute, rug wool and acrylic yarns provide interesting variations in texture.

Activity — Making a macrame plant hanger

You will need

- 1 ball of 3 ply macrame jute
- 8 wooden beads (with a hole large enough for the jute to pass through easily)
- Scissors
- Tape measure
- Colourful plastic or wooden pot, 20 cm in diameter

Method

(1) Cut eight pieces of jute each 6 m long.
(2) Cut two pieces of jute each 60 cm long.
(3) Find the middle of the eight pieces of jute.

Square knot for 20 cm to form the handle from the centre, using the two small pieces of jute.

Square knotting the handle. Cords are kept taut by placing one end in a cupboard and shutting the door. The other end is lent on by the worker.

(4) Bend the handle in half, then wrap knot the 16 yarns together.
(5) Make four *sinnets* of square knots using groups of four yarns (two *filler yarns* and two *knotting yarns*), 15 cm long. (A sinnet is a length of knotting consisting of the two outside knotting yarns and two inside filler yarns.)

Sinnets are knotted using alternating square knots. The outside cords are kept from tangling by winding them up and securing them with an elastic band.

Right: The completed plant hanger. Use a brightly coloured pot to enhance the design. Now use the skills you have learnt to make a wall hanging or a plant hanger of a different design.

(6) Pass four beads through each of the sets of yarns and continue knotting, using either half knots or square knots, for another 20 cm.

(7) Repeat step 6.

(8) To form the *cradle* for the pot, alternate filler yarns with knotting yarns, using one square knot to join sinnet 1 with sinnet 2, and sinnet 2 with sinnet 3, and so on.

(9) Leave 10 cm of yarn, and repeat step 8 for each sinnet.

(10) Wrap knot all 16 yarns together, 10 cm from the last row of square knots.

(11) Cut all cords off at the botton, 15 cm from the wrap knot. Brush out tassel.

Helpful hints

- Bundle knotting yarns and bind them using an elastic band. This shortens the knotting yarns and so prevents tangles while working.
- Once the handle is made, hang it from a window latch or door handle to make knotting the sinnet easier.
- Check the pot measurement to ensure that you start the alternate knotting at the top edge of the pot.
- Use an old comb or dog's brush to brush out the tassel.

Synthetic fibres

Spanzelle

Another elastomeric fibre is *Spanzelle* which stretches and returns to its original shape as does *Lycra*. The yarn is strong and hardwearing, resists perspiration and is light in weight.

Dynel

The trade name of a modacrylic fibre. The fibres are treated to give the appearance of human hair. Used mainly for doll's hair, wigs and fur fabric. It is flame resistant.

Polyethylene

A fibre made from cheap crude oil products. It is non-absorbent, is not damaged by sunlight or bleaches and has good elastic properties. Used for plastic bags, carpets and fake furs.

Polypropylene

Has the same properties as polyethylene. Used mainly for waterproof raincoats, sails, carpets and stockings.

Teklan

Teklan is a modacrylic fibre. It is widely used for furnishing fabrics for public buildings, for wigs and hair pieces and for children's night wear as it is flame retardant.

Glass fibres

Fine monofilament fibres produced by extruding molten glass through a spinneret. These fibres are spun and woven to produce non-flammable curtain fabrics, especially for theatres and public buildings. The glass fibre is not suitable for clothing, as it is brittle and causes skin irritation.

Alginate

A fibre made from seaweed which dissolves in water. It is obviously unsuitable for clothing and is used for such things as surgical sutures, which dissolve in body fluids a few days after an operation, and in the manufacture of socks and stockings. A row of alginate is knitted between socks and the long length of socks is then placed in water, which dissolves the alginate and separates the socks.

Activity

Can you think of any other process in clothing manufacture where production time could be saved by using alginate?

Identifying fibres and fabrics

Sometimes we need to be able to identify a fibre or fabric in order to decide how it should be cared for or what it can be used for. There are several ways of doing this. In each case, compare your results with the fibre identification charts on pp. 156–8.

Burning test

The easiest way to identify a fibre or fabric is by a simple *burning test*. Observe very closely what happens to a fabric sample when held (1) near a flame, (2) in the flame and (3) on being removed from the flame.

Warning: This test should be carried out only under your teacher's supervision. It should be done over a sink, holding the fabric sample with tweezers.

Answer the following questions:

(1) Does the sample melt near the flame?
(2) How do the fibres burn, and what colour is the flame?
(3) Is smoke given off? Is there a distinct odour?
(4) What is the remaining ash like — a hard bead or soft grey ash?

Microscopic tests

Information about fibres can be gained by observing them under the microscope in longitudinal and cross-sectional views. Sketch what you see under low power and then under high power. For the best results, use undyed fibres on a black background. Set up the slide for a cross-sectional view, using a metallic plate with small holes, and follow the directions below.

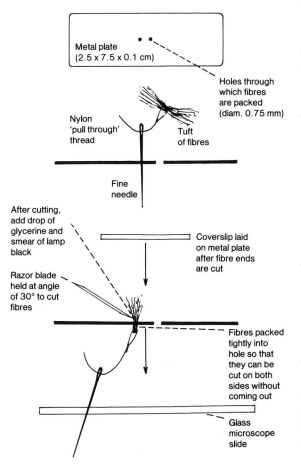

Use of metal plate for cutting fibre sections

Metal plate (2.5 x 7.5 x 0.1 cm)

Holes through which fibres are packed (diam. 0.75 mm)

Nylon 'pull through' thread

Tuft of fibres

Fine needle

After cutting, add drop of glycerine and smear of lamp black

Coverslip laid on metal plate after fibre ends are cut

Razor blade held at angle of 30° to cut fibres

Fibres packed tightly into hole so that they can be cut on both sides without coming out

Glass microscope slide

Making cross-sections of fibres for identification under the microscope

Sodium hydroxide test (adding alkali)

Add some fibres to 10 ml of weak sodium hydroxide solution, and note whether dissolving or swelling occurs over a thirty-minute period. *Warning:* Make sure that the solution does not come in contact with your skin.

Acetone test

Pour acetone over fibres in a small dish. Note whether they swell, disappear or become soft.

Hydrochloric acid test (adding acid)

Pour hydrochloric acid over fibres in a test tube. Note any changes after thirty minutes. *Warning:* Hydrochloric acid needs to be handled with great care. Make sure that it does not come in contact with your skin.

Shirlastain test

Shirlastain 'A' is best used on a colourless sample of fibres or fabric. The fabric sample should be wetted thoroughly, immersed in a cold solution of the stain, stirred, dried and compared with the comparison chart of colours (e.g. wool — yellow, cotton — lavender).

Activity

Using the *fibre identification charts* on the following pages, try to identify a number of samples of fibres and fabrics that are unknown to you.

Words to remember

alpaca	Dynel
cashmere	Teklan
llama	Spanzelle
Angora	polypropylene
mohair	polyethylene
upholstery	alginate
coir	suture
kapok	sodium hydroxide
hemp	hydrochloric acid
jute	identification
macrame	acetone
sinnet	longitudinal
wrap knot	cross-section
square knot	odour
bustle	Shirlastain
sisal	

Fibre identification charts

(1) Natural fibres

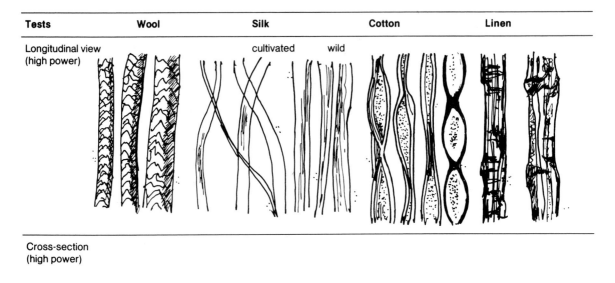

Tests	Wool	Silk		Cotton	Linen
Longitudinal view (high power)		cultivated	wild		
Cross-section (high power)					

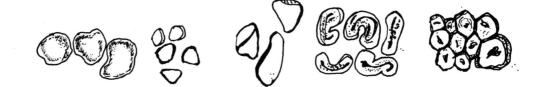

	Wool	Silk	Cotton	Linen
Burning tests in flame	Smoulders	Burns slowly with yellow flame	Burns quickly with yellow flame	Burns with yellow flame, tends to flare
Out of flame	Self-extinguishing	Self-extinguishing	Continues to burn	Continues to burn
Odour	Burning feathers or hair	Burning hair	Burning paper	Burning paper
Residue	Ash inflated, bulbous and soft	Bead-like, crushable grey ash	Light, feathery, grey ash	Similar to cotton, but more ash
Boiling with 10% solution of sodium hydroxide	Dissolves / Brown/black	Dissolves / No colouration	Swells / No colouration	Swells / No colouration
Acetone	No reaction	No reaction	No reaction	No reaction
Concentrated hydrochloric acid	No reaction	Disintegrates and dissolves	No reaction	No reaction
Shirlastain A	Golden yellow	Orange brown	Lavender	Violet/blue

(2) Synthetic fibres

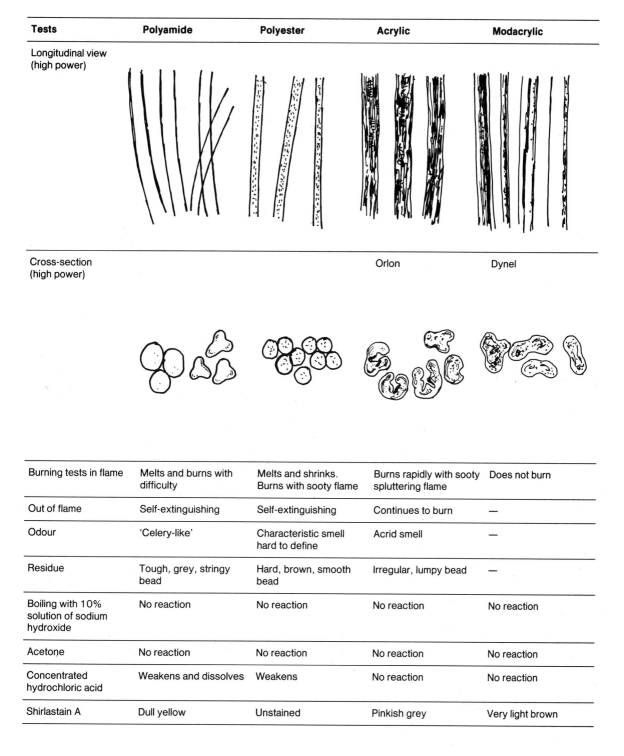

Tests	Polyamide	Polyester	Acrylic	Modacrylic
Longitudinal view (high power)				
Cross-section (high power)			Orlon	Dynel
Burning tests in flame	Melts and burns with difficulty	Melts and shrinks. Burns with sooty flame	Burns rapidly with sooty spluttering flame	Does not burn
Out of flame	Self-extinguishing	Self-extinguishing	Continues to burn	—
Odour	'Celery-like'	Characteristic smell hard to define	Acrid smell	—
Residue	Tough, grey, stringy bead	Hard, brown, smooth bead	Irregular, lumpy bead	—
Boiling with 10% solution of sodium hydroxide	No reaction	No reaction	No reaction	No reaction
Acetone	No reaction	No reaction	No reaction	No reaction
Concentrated hydrochloric acid	Weakens and dissolves	Weakens	No reaction	No reaction
Shirlastain A	Dull yellow	Unstained	Pinkish grey	Very light brown

(3) Regenerated fibres

Tests	Viscose rayon	Triacetate	Cellulose acetate
Longitudinal view (high power)			

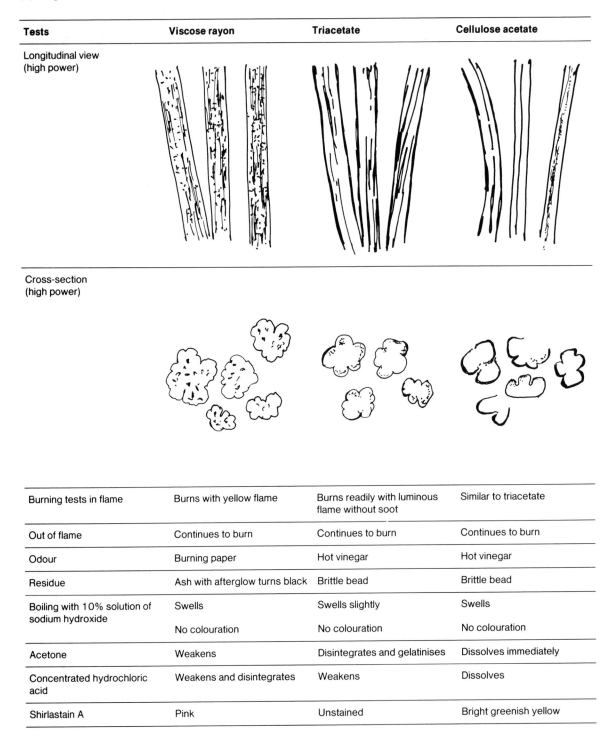

Tests	Viscose rayon	Triacetate	Cellulose acetate
Cross-section (high power)			
Burning tests in flame	Burns with yellow flame	Burns readily with luminous flame without soot	Similar to triacetate
Out of flame	Continues to burn	Continues to burn	Continues to burn
Odour	Burning paper	Hot vinegar	Hot vinegar
Residue	Ash with afterglow turns black	Brittle bead	Brittle bead
Boiling with 10% solution of sodium hydroxide	Swells No colouration	Swells slightly No colouration	Swells No colouration
Acetone	Weakens	Disintegrates and gelatinises	Dissolves immediately
Concentrated hydrochloric acid	Weakens and disintegrates	Weakens	Dissolves
Shirlastain A	Pink	Unstained	Bright greenish yellow

Revision exercises

(1) Match the words and clues:

(a) Cashmere   ( ) Used for macrame work.

(b) Angora   ( ) Used for padding bustles.

(c) Horsehair   ( ) Used for mooring rope.

(d) Sinnet   ( ) The coarse hair of coconut

(e) Jute   ( ) A smell

(f) Coir   ( ) Used for wigs and dolls' hair.

(g) Hemp   ( ) The name of a species of rabbit

(h) Dynel   ( ) A macrame chain of knots

(i) Odour   ( ) Fibres from a goat

(j) Longitudinal   ( ) A soft fibre grown inside a seed pod

(k) Kapok   ( ) A view of fibres under the microscope

(2) Choose the word that is out of place in the group:

e.g. Cashmere, Angora, Dynel, Llama

Answer: Dynel, as it is a synthetic fibre; the other three are protein fibres.

(a) Teklan, Spanzelle, Sisal, Dynel
(b) Alginate, Coir, Suture, Seaweed
(c) Sinnet, Wrap knot, Jute, Mohair
(d) Mohair, Sisal, Cashmere, Camel
(e) Alpaca, Kapok, Hemp, Jute
(f) Polyester, Melts, Shrinks, Soft ash
(g) Irregular lumpy bead, Acrylic, Rayon, Sooty flame
(h) Irregular lumpy bead, polyamide, Celery-like smell, Self-extinguishing flame

Answers

p. 3   *Across* 4. alginate, 6. terylene, 9. fibre, 10. sisal, 11. wool, 12. lurex
       Down 1. sisal, 2. camel, 3. courlene, 4. alpacas, 5. goat, 7. yarn, 8. nylon, 9. flax, 10. silk

p. 14   **Extension activity 1:** protection, Moslem, cicatrisation, roles, revolution, ochre, cottage, designer

p. 42   **Revision exercises:** *(1) Double decker:* animal, vegetable, sepia, lichens, dyes, mauve, Nylon, wool, mordant, alum, tin, iron

p. 43   *(2) What am I?:* vat dye *(3) What am I?:* mordant *(4) Skill test:* (1) b (2) c (3) d (4) a (5) a (6) c (7) d (8) a (9) b (10) c

p. 55   **Complete the sentence:** To be a wise consumer, read care labels before buying.

p. 61   **Revision exercise 1:** (1) c (2) a (3) b (4) c (5) d (6) a (7) d (8) b (9) a (10) a

p. 61   **Revision exercise 2:** (1) nylon (2) drop spinning (3) roving (4) cotton (5) wool (6) K twist (7) blending (8) drawing

p. 62   **Revision exercise 3:** multifilament, open-end spinning, natural, Orlon, fibres, silk, loop, heat set, metallic, thermoplastic, nylon, twist

p. 74   **Revision exercises** *(1) Double confusion* (2) weaving/knitting (3) a latchet needle (4) warp/weft (5) tricot/raschel (6) tufting/pile weave (7) heat/pressure (8) leno/gauze (9) heddle/shuttle (10) basket/plain

p. 89   **Fashion crossword:** *Across* 1. silhouette, 2. drape, 3. darts, 4. jodhpur, 5. mandarin, 6. satin, 7. vertical, 8. kimono
       Down 1. accordion, 2. horizontal, 3. blue, 4. texture, 5. red, 6. padding, 7. proportion

p. 111 **Complete the sentence:** Buy all your clothing to suit your personality.

p. 141 **Revision exercise 6:** (a) interior, antique, life, colour, proportion, line, analogous, harmony. (c) function

p. 147 **Revision exercise 1:** (1) elastomeric (2) Dacron (3) Orlon (4) monofilament (5) melt spinning (6) synthetic (7) spinneret (8) regenerated (9) aluminium (10) polyvinyl chloride

p. 147 **Revision exercise 2:** Lycra, viscose, Orlon, nylon, Dacron, Crimplene, Terylene, acetate, rayon, Dralon

p. 159 **Revision exercises** (1) e,c,g,f,i,h,b,d,a,k,j
       (2) (a) Sisal — it is a cellulosic fibre; the other three are synthetic fibres. (b) Coir — comes from coconut hair; the other three are algae. (c) Mohair — the other three are related to macrame work. (d) Sisal — as it is a plant fibre; the others are protein fibres. (e) Alpaca — comes from an animal source; the other 3 are from plant origin.. (f) Soft ash — polyester melts and shrinks but leaves a lumpy bead.

Acknowledgements

The authors and publishers are grateful to the following for permission to reproduce copyright material:

NASA p. 4; The Commissioner of Police of the Metropolis, London p. 7; Herald & Weekly Times pp. 8, 54, 70; RCA Limited p. 9; Associated Press pp. 9, 13; United Press International p. 12; International Wool Secretariat p. 20; Keystone p. 24; Tootal Craft p. 26; National Publicity Studios, Wellington, New Zealand p. 27; International Society for Educational Information, Japan p. 29; Australian National Gallery pp. 34, 124; Actil Pty Ltd p. 36; Braun UK Ltd p. 47; C&A p. 48; George Black Textile Group Pty Ltd p. 64; Myer Southern Stores pp. 133, 134; Allan A. Hedges p. 142.

Illustrations by Betina Ogden
Cover illustration by Nicola Shaw

While every care has been taken to trace and acknowledge copyright, the publishers tender their apologies for any accidental infringement where copyright has proved untraceable. They would be pleased to come to a suitable arrangement with the rightful owner in each case.

Index